Canadian Mathematics Competition

PROBLEMS
PROBLEMS
PROBLEMS

VOLUME 2

Canadian Mathematics Competition
Faculty of Mathematics
University of Waterloo
Waterloo, Ontario, Canada
1989

Published by
Waterloo Mathematics Foundation
University of Waterloo
Waterloo, Ontario, Canada
N2L 3G1

Telephone: (519) 885-1211, extension 3030
Fax: (519) 746-6592

Canadian Cataloguing in Publication Data

Main entry under title:

Problems, problems, problems

"Canadian Mathematics Competition".
For use in high schools
ISBN 0-921418-00-0 (v. 1)   ISBN 0-921418-01-9 (v. 2)

1. Mathematics--Examinations, questions, etc.
I. Waterloo Mathematics Foundation. II. Canadian
Mathematics Competition.

QA139.P76 1988   510'.76   C88-090190-X

Printed by Graphic Services, University of Waterloo

Introduction

Problems, Problems, Problems Volume 2 is the second volume in a series of Problems Books compiled by the Canadian Mathematics Competition, Faculty of Mathematics, University of Waterloo. The aim of the series is twofold: to enable a greater number of students to experience the joy of problem solving, and to provide a useful supplement to school curriculum.

As in the first volume, questions have been selected and organized by topic, and by degree of difficulty. Half of the problems are presented in multiple choice format, half in full solution format. For easy reference, we have identified the questions by contest year. Although the focus is on topics that parallel the programs of grades 9, 10, and 11, students in other grades may enjoy the challenge these problems provide. Our goal, then, is to offer a ready source of problems for both contest preparation, as well as classroom enrichment.

Since its inception twenty-six years ago, over one *million* students have participated in the Canadian Mathematics Competition. Furthermore, many mathematics teachers have made an outstanding contribution to our contest committees. The Competition salutes the many dedicated teachers who contribute their time and talents working with young mathematicians in the schools of Canada.

We wish to recognize those who assisted in the preparation of this book. Members of the Department of Mathematics at Beamsville District High School, especially Don Roberts, Vicky Dale of Lo-Ellen Park Secondary School in Sudbury, and members of the C.M.C. Executive, including Lloyd Auckland, Ed Anderson, Larry Davidson, Ron Dunkley, Barry Ferguson, and Ron Scoins all contributed to the manuscript. The technical production was performed by Betty Weber, Rachel Hotson, and Gayle Morris.

We hope that readers enjoy the book. Some parents have joined their children in solving our mathematics problems. We are confident that the new problems book will provide many interesting hours for those who like a mathematical challenge.

Canadian Mathematics Competition
Waterloo, Ontario, Canada
April, 1989

Contents

Contest References

Each question in the book has been given a reference number of the form "year-contest-question number". For example, 1983-C-19 indicates question 19 from the 1983 Cayley Contest. The contest abbreviations are: G - Gauss (Grades 7 and 8), P - Pascal (Grade 9), C - Cayley (Grade 10), F - Fermat (Grade 11) and J - Junior. (Prior to 1981, the Pascal, Cayley, and Fermat Contests were combined into one paper called the Junior Mathematics Contest.)

Questions

In playing Space Invaders, Janet shot down 12 of the 25 Invaders with 50 shots. One successful shot destroys one Invader. What percentage of Janet's shots hit Invaders?

Percentages

Multiple Choice Questions

1971-J-1
1. 1000% of 2 equals

    (A) 2000   (B) 1002   (C) 200   (D) 20   (E) 0.002

1983-P-6
2. To the nearest whole number, 115% of 15 is

    (A) 15   (B) 16   (C) 17   (D) 18   (E) none of these

1975-J-1
3. $\frac{1}{10}$ of 1% is

    (A) 10   (B) 0.1   (C) 0.01   (D) 0.001   (E) 0.0001

1980-G-8
4. 0.75 % of 264 is

(A) 352   (B) 198   (C) 3.52   (D) 1.98   (E) 0.198

1979-G-17
5. In a class of 30 students, 40% wear glasses. Three of those wearing glasses are left-handed. Of those wearing glasses, the percent who are left-handed is

(A) 10   (B) 25   (C) $7\frac{1}{2}$ (D) 3   (E) 4

1975-G-3
6. On an examination, 13 students passed and 3 students failed. The failure rate, in per cent, is

(A) $18\frac{3}{4}$ (B) $\frac{300}{13}$ (C) $\frac{1300}{3}$ (D) $23\frac{1}{3}$ (E) $43\frac{1}{3}$

1979-G-21
7. A man borrowed $3500 and a year later paid back the loan plus interest with a cheque for $4200. The annual rate of interest, in percent, paid for the loan was

(A) 700   (B) 83.3   (C) 20   (D) 120   (E) 16.6

1976-J-2
8. If 2% of a number is 8, then the number is

(A) 0.16   (B) 4   (C) 16   (D) 400   (E) 800

1975-J-10
9. The price of an article is reduced by 20%. In order to restore the reduced price to the original value, the reduced price must be increased by

(A) 20%   (B) $22\frac{1}{2}$%   (C) 25%   (D) 30%   (E) 15%

1980-G-18
10. A bill to pay for a T-shirt, on which there is a 7% sales tax, comes to $3.73. The price of the shirt before tax is

(A) $3.99   (B) $3.66   (C) $3.49   (D) $3.47   (E) $2.19

1980-G-14
11. A ski shop offered a 25% discount on a pair of skis that originally sold for $90.00. The new price was then reduced by 10%. The final sale price was

(A) $31.50   (B) $55.00   (C) $81.00   (D) $58.50   (E) $60.75

1984-F-11

12. A team's record is 20 wins and 25 losses. To qualify for the playoffs a team must win 60% of its games played. The number of wins of the remaining 15 games necessary for the team to qualify is

   (A) 4   (B) 10   (C) 12   (D) 15   (E) impossible to achieve

1976-G-26

13. On a $10 purchase, Tom was offered 3 successive discounts of 20%, 10%, and 5% in any order he wished. He selected the discounts in the order 5%, 10%, and 20%. Which of the following order of discounts would have been better for him?

   (A) 20, 10, 5   (B) 20, 5, 10   (C) 5, 20, 10   (D) 10, 20, 5   (E) none of these

1974-J-7

14. In each of three successive years, the cost of living increases by 10%. The percentage increase over the three years is

   (A) 30   (B) 130   (C) 33.1   (D) 33   (E) 133.1

1963-J-25

15. Mr. Jones sold 2 pipes at $1.20 each. Based on the cost, the profit on one was 20% and the loss on the other was 20%. On the sale of the pipes he

   (A) broke even   (B) lost 4 cents   (C) gained 4 cents
   (D) lost 10 cents   (E) gained 10 cents

1972-J-9

16. A man has a rectangular patio in his garden. He decides to enlarge it by increasing both length and width by 10%. The percentage increase in area is

   (A) 10   (B) 20   (C) 21   (D) 40   (E) 121

1985-G8-20

17. The sides of a cube are doubled in length. The increase in the volume of the new cube from the original cube is

   (A) 900%   (B) 700%   (C) 400%   (D) 200%   (E) 100%

1979-J-19

18. A student mistakenly divides a number by 5 instead of multiplying it by 5. The percentage error, the ratio of the amount of the error to the correct value expressed as a percent, is

   (A) 4   (B) 25   (C) 80   (D) 96   (E) 2400

Full Solution Questions

1968-J-1

1. Find $\frac{1}{2}$% of 900.

1975-J-1

2. Find $\frac{2}{3}$% of 600.

1972-J-2

3. What is the value of 20 increased by 200% of itself?

1978-G-12

4. The selling price of a coat, which normally sells for $55.00, was reduced by 20% during the spring sale. Since the coat still didn't sell the sale price was reduced by 10%. What was the total reduction from the original selling price?

1985-G8-9

5. In playing Space Invaders, Janet shot down 12 of the 25 Invaders with 50 shots. One successful shot destroys one Invader. What percentage of Janet's shots hit Invaders?

1984-G-9

6. The yearly interest paid on a loan of $1200 is $180. What is the annual rate of interest, expressed as a percent?

7. If 10% of x is equal to 25% of 16, what is the value of x?

1975-G-13

8. When 4131 people attended a concert, the concert hall was 90% full. What is the capacity of the hall?

1982-P-10

9. In the latest We-All-Win (?) Lottery draw, 0.08% of the tickets sold won prizes. How many tickets were sold if two prizes were won?

10. A baseball team has won 50 games out of 75 played and has 45 games still to play. How many of the remaining games must it win in order that its percentage of games won for the entire season will be 60%?

1976-G-5

11. Joe Blow receives 10% off every purchase at Harry's Hardware. Unfortunately, he must pay 7% sales tax on the reduced price. How much would Joe pay for a drill whose regular price is $14.00?

1975-G-20

12. The cost of a can of wax, including 5% sales tax, is $1.20. If the price of a can of wax, without sales tax, is reduced to 70% of its original cost, what is the new price before the tax is added?

1978-G-10

13. A Big McBurger is 30% beef, 30% cereal, 20% water, and 20% ingredients untouched by human hands. If one pound equals 16 ounces, determine the water content, in ounces, of a $\frac{1}{4}$ pound Big McBurger.

1986-G8-18

14. Suppose the value of one American dollar is 30% more than the value of one Canadian dollar. An American tourist in Canada purchases a $35 souvenir with thirty American dollars. What should his change, in Canadian dollars, be from this purchase?

1977-G-23

15. Harry Wirks earns a salary of $360 per week for a 44 hour week. His weekly salary is increased by 10% and his hours are reduced by 10%. Calculate his new hourly salary.

1976-J-13

16. The length of a rectangle is increased by 15% and the width is decreased by 20%. Find the percentage change in the area of the rectangle.

1986-G7-22

17. On a test consisting of 30 questions, Sue had 50% more right answers than she had wrong answers. Each answer was either right or wrong. How many questions did she answer correctly?

1984-C-20

18. Mr. Afton has an income which is five-eighths of Miss Benson's. Mr. Afton's expenses are one-half those of Miss Benson, and Mr. Afton saves 40% of his income. What percentage of her income does Miss Benson save?

Tim, Mary, and Sue have 73 cassette tapes altogether. Mary has 5 more tapes than Tim and Tim has 7 more than Sue. How many tapes does Mary have?

Linear Equations

Multiple Choice Questions

1989-C-2
1. If $15x + 20 = 25$, then the value of x is

 (A) -10 (B) $-\frac{1}{3}$ (C) $\frac{1}{3}$ (D) $\frac{5}{7}$ (E) 3

1982-F-1
2. If $0.02y = 1$, then y equals

 (A) 0.02   (B) 0.05   (C) 0.5   (D) 5   (E) 50

1980-J-1
3. If $\frac{2}{3}x = 0.6$, then x equals

 (A) 0.4   (B) 0.9   (C) 4   (D) 0.09   (E) 9

1985-P-14
4. If $\frac{4}{5}x = 9$, then $2x$ equals

    (A) 11.25   (B) 22.5   (C) 45   (D) 82   (E) none of these

1968-J-3
5. If $5x - 3 = ax$, then x equals

    (A) $a - \frac{5}{3}$ (B) $3 - \frac{a}{5}$ (C) $\frac{5}{a+3}$ (D) $\frac{3}{a-5}$ (E) $\frac{3}{5-a}$

1975-J-5
6. If $x = 2k$ and $y = \frac{4}{k}$, then y equals

    (A) $8x$ (B) $\frac{8}{x}$ (C) $\frac{2}{x}$ (D) $2x$ (E) 8

1979-J-2
7. If $a = 2b$ and $b = 4c$, then $a + 2b - 8c$ equals

    (A) $24c$ (B) $8c$ (C) $4c$ (D) $12c$ (E) $16c$

1979-G-16
8. If $x = 7$ and $xy = 91$, the value of $x + 2y$ is

    (A) 189   (B) 27   (C) 33   (D) 220   (E) 40

1988-G8-2
9. When half a number is increased by 15, the result is 39. The original number is

    (A) 12   (B) 27   (C) 48   (D) 54   (E) 108

1985-C-12
10. If $\frac{1}{x} = \frac{5}{a}$ and $x = \frac{c}{6}$, then the value of $\frac{c}{a}$ is

    (A) 30   (B) $\frac{5}{6}$ (C) $\frac{1}{5}$ (D) $\frac{1}{6}$ (E) $\frac{6}{5}$

1982-P-6

11. The value of x in the plane figure shown is

(A) 30   (B) 60   (C) 90
(D) 120   (E) 150

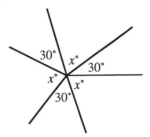

1989-P-18

12. If $3x + 7 = x^2 + k = 7x + 15$, then k equals

(A) -45 (B) -3 (C) -2 (D) 2   (E) 25

1982-F-16

13. If s, p, and r are positive, and $s = p + \frac{1}{2}rp^2$, then r is equal to

(A) $\dfrac{2s - 2p}{p^2}$ (B) $2p^2s - 2p^3$ (C) $\dfrac{2 - 2ps}{p^2}$ (D) $\dfrac{2 + 2ps}{p^2}$ (E) $\frac{1}{2}p^2s - \frac{1}{2}p^3$

1978-J-4

14. A pen and pencil together cost $1.40. The pen costs one dollar more than the pencil. The cost, in cents, of the pencil is

(A) 120   (B) 100   (C) 40   (D) 30   (E) 20

1983-P-8

15. If a wire 58 units long is bent into the symmetrical arrow shape shown, then the value of y is

(A) $10\frac{1}{4}$ (B) 5   (C) $4\frac{1}{4}$
(D) 6   (E) none of these

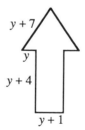

16. The reciprocal of $\frac{3x}{4}$ is $\frac{1}{12}$. The value of x is

(A) $\frac{1}{9}$ (B) 9   (C) $\frac{1}{3}$ (D) 16   (E) $\frac{1}{16}$

1986-P-17

17. If $(a, b) \blacklozenge (c, d) = ac + bd$ and $(x, 3) \blacklozenge (-2, 5) = 3$, then the value of x is

    (A) -9 (B) -6 (C) $\frac{9}{5}$ (D) $\frac{13}{3}$ (E) 6

1973-J-9

18. If $y = \dfrac{x-2}{x+1}$, then x is equal to

    (A) $\dfrac{2+y}{1-y}$ (B) $\dfrac{y-2}{y+1}$ (C) $\dfrac{y+2}{y+1}$ (D) $\dfrac{y+2}{y-1}$ (E) $\dfrac{2-y}{1-y}$

1984-F-6

19. It requires 200 ml of liquid to fill a glass to 0.8 of its capacity. The capacity of the glass, in ml, is

    (A) 225   (B) 160   (C) 360   (D) 240   (E) 250

1988-F-11

20. If $\dfrac{a}{x-b} = \dfrac{b}{x-a}$, $a \neq b$, then x is equal to

    (A) $b - a$ (B) $a - b$ (C) $a + b$ (D) 1 (E) $-a - b$

1965-J-12

21. A brick and a five ounce weight on one pan of a balance will balance evenly with three-quarters of a pound and three-quarters of a brick. The brick's weight, in pounds, is (one pound = 16 ounces)

    (A) 28   (B) $\dfrac{7}{4}$ (C) $\dfrac{17}{3}$ (D) $\dfrac{43}{16}$ (E) 8

1975-J-13

22. A tank is $\dfrac{1}{6}$ full of gasoline. If 2 gallons are added, then the tank is $\dfrac{1}{4}$ full. The total capacity of the tank, in gallons, is

    (A) 6   (B) 8   (C) 12   (D) 24   (E) 30

1965-J-3

23. The largest angle of a given triangle is 35 degrees more than the smallest angle, and the smallest angle is 10 degrees less than the third angle. The number of degrees in the smallest angle is

    (A) 35   (B) 45   (C) 50   (D) 55   (E) 60

24. If $(-1 - x)^3 = 1$, then a solution for x is

    (A) 0   (B) 1   (C) -1 (D) 2   (E) -2

Full Solution Questions

1969-J-1
1. Solve the equation $2x + 5 = 9x - 13$.

1981-J-3
2. Find the value of x if $0.4x = \frac{2}{3}$.

1983-F-7
3. If $ax + c = bx$, where a, b, c, are distinct positive numbers, find x.

1980-J-9
4. If -2 is substituted for x in the expression $x^3 - 4x^2 - kx - 20$ and the result is 0, find the value of k.

1981-J-11
5. Given that $a = 30 - bc$, where b is a constant, and that $a = 12$ when $c = 12$, determine the value of c when $a = 21$.

1986-P-15
6. If $\frac{1}{3} + \frac{1}{4} + \frac{1}{n} = 1$, find the value of n.

1984-P-16
7. Given the equation $y = \frac{2x - 3}{x + 6}$, find the value of x when $y = -2$.

1984-P-20
8. What is the value of $p + q$ if $\frac{p}{q} = -1$?

1986-P-20
9. If $x : y = 3 : 2$ and $x + 3y = 27$, find x and y?

1974-J-17
10. If $ab = 16$, $\frac{b}{c} = \frac{1}{3}$, and $\frac{c}{a} = 12$, find the value of b.

1966-J-25
11. The values of a, b, and c are such that $a - b = b - c = 3$. Determine the value of $a^2 - 2b^2 + c^2$.

1989-P-11

12. If $\frac{5}{6}$ of a number is 60, what is $\frac{3}{4}$ of the number?

1989-C-11

13. Tim, Mary, and Sue have 73 cassette tapes altogether. Mary has 5 more tapes than Tim and Tim has 7 more than Sue. Find the number of tapes that Mary has.

1988-P-14

14. If the reciprocal of $\left(\frac{1}{x} - 1\right)$ is –2, find x.

1985-P-15

15. A secretary buys an equal number of 35 cent and 30 cent stamps for $22.75. Find the total number of stamps purchased.

1980-J-8

16. A grocer buys oranges at 3 for 25 cents. He plans to sell them at 5 for 45 cents. In order to make a profit of $3.00, how many must he sell?

1976-J-9

17. The grand prizewinner of a lottery won $\frac{7}{10}$ of the total prize money available. Shortly thereafter, she spent $\frac{3}{4}$ of her winnings, and still had $2100 left. Find the total amount of prize money available in the lottery.

1983-P-4

18. In the diagram, find, in degrees, the measure of the largest angle.

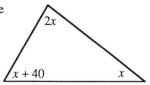

1983-P-15

19. If $2x - 5$ is exactly 2 greater than $-3x + 4$, find the value of x.

1985-C-5

20. A rope of length 64 metres is cut into three pieces. The second piece is three times as long as the first, and the third is four times as long as the second. Find the length, in metres, of the shortest piece.

1987-P-11

21. In isosceles triangle PQR, the length of PQ is three times the length of PR. If the perimeter of the triangle is 35, find the length of PQ.

1982-F-5

22. In the parallelogram shown, find the value of y.

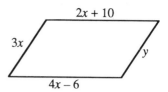

1973-J-7

23. If $\frac{1}{3} > \frac{1}{5} > \frac{1}{c}$, and the difference between the first two fractions equals the difference between the last two fractions, find the value of c.

24. A number N is doubled and increased by 5. When this quantity is doubled, the result is 38. Find the value of N.

25. If two times a number is increased by 8, the result is 2 less than three times the number. Find the number.

A window consists of a rectangle surmounted by a semicircle. The rectangular portion has a width of 2 metres and a height of 1 metre. What is the perimeter of the window?

Circumferences of Circles

Multiple Choice Questions

1979-G7-7

1. The radius of a circle having circumference 6π units is

   (A) 3   (B) 4π (C) $\dfrac{3}{\pi}$ (D) 3π (E) 4

1977-G-17

2. A piece of string, 40 cm long, is formed into a circle with the ends of the string touching each other. The radius of the circle, in cm, is

   (A) 40π (B) 80π (C) $\dfrac{20}{\pi}$ (D) $\dfrac{40}{\pi}$ (E) $\sqrt{\dfrac{80}{\pi}}$

1970-J-8

3. Given a circle of perimeter 3 units, its area in square units is

    (A) $\dfrac{3\pi}{2}$ (B) $\dfrac{9}{4\pi}$ (C) $\dfrac{9}{\pi}$ (D) $\dfrac{9\pi}{4}$ (E) none of these

1985-C-7

4. A playground is designed by placing semicircles of
    fencing on each of the four sides of a square whose
    sides are each $2x$ metres long. The number of
    metres of fencing required is

    (A) $4\pi x$ (B) $4\pi^2 x$ (C) $2\pi x$
    (D) $2\pi x^2$ (E) none of these

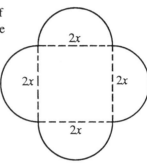

1970-J-17

5. A square and a circle have equal perimeters. The ratio of the area of the square to the
    area of the circle is

    (A) $1:1$ (B) $\pi:1$ (C) $\pi:2$ (D) $\pi:4$ (E) $1:4$

1968-J-13

6. In the diagram, circular arcs PQ, QR, and ST,
    have centres T, S, and Q respectively. If PT
    equals one unit, then the perimeter of figure
    $PQRST$ is

    (A) $4+\pi$ (B) $2+\pi$ (C) 2π
    (D) $2+2\pi$ (E) none of these

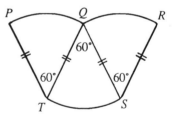

1971-J-10

7. Four equal semicircles are cut out of a square as in
    the diagram. If the perimeter of the original square
    was 60, the perimeter of the figure remaining is

    (A) $40+10\pi$ (B) $60-10\pi$ (C) $225-\dfrac{25\pi}{2}$
    (D) $40+25\pi$ (E) none of these

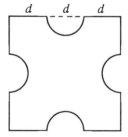

1968-J-6

8. If the radius of a circle is increased by one unit, the ratio of the new circumference to the new diameter is

(A) $(\pi + 2) : 1$ (B) $(2\pi + 1) : \pi$ (C) $\pi : 1$ (D) $(2\pi - 1) : 2$ (E) $(\pi - 2) : 1$

1982-P- 20

9. A circle of radius r is rolled around the outside of a rectangle of perimeter p, always maintaining contact with the rectangle. The distance travelled by the centre of the circle, when the circle has travelled once around the rectangle, is

(A) $p + 4r$ (B) $p + 8\pi r$ (C) $p + \pi r$ (D) $p + 2\pi r$ (E) $p + 8r$

1965-J-11

10. Of the following statements the one that is incorrect is:

(A) Doubling the radius of a given circle doubles its area.
(B) Doubling the altitude of a given triangle doubles its area.
(C) Doubling the base of a given rectangle doubles the area.
(D) Doubling the numerator of a fraction doubles the fraction.
(E) Doubling a given number may make it less than it originally was.

1985-P-25

11. A manufacturer sells clear plastic tape on a spool with radius 1 cm. The tape is 0.02 cm thick and 1.5 cm wide. The combined radius of the spool and the tape is 3 cm. Of the following, the best approximation of the length of tape on the spool, in metres, is

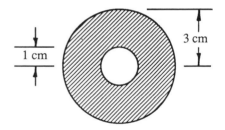

(A) 1.6   (B) 5.1   (C) 6.3
(D) 9.4   (E) 12.6

1965-J-18

12. The circumference of a circle is 100 inches. The side of a square inscribed in this circle, in inches, is

(A) $\dfrac{25\sqrt{2}}{\pi}$ (B) $\dfrac{50\sqrt{2}}{\pi}$ (C) $\dfrac{100}{\pi}$ (D) $\dfrac{100\sqrt{2}}{\pi}$ (E) $\dfrac{50}{\pi}$

1989-F-20

13. A cable is formed by combining 7 circular wires, touching each other as shown. These wires are held in place by a taut band around the system. If each wire has a radius of 2 units, then the length of the band is

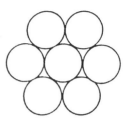

   (A) 12π (B) 24   (C) $24 + 4\pi$
   (D) 36   (E) $24 + 8\pi$

Full Solution Questions

1978-G-9

1. Find the circumference of a circular race track whose radius is 50 m.

1975-G-21

2. If the difference between the radii of two circles is 10 cm, find the difference between their circumferences.

1977-J-9

3. Find the area of a circle whose circumference is π.

1983-G-22

4. The diagram shows a soup can with the top and bottom removed. The diameter of the can is 5 cm and the height is 12 cm. Find the perimeter of the rectangle formed when the can is cut along the dotted line.

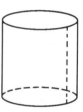

1986-C-15

5. An arc is one-sixth of the circumference of the circle whose area is 144π. Find the length of the arc.

1974-J-10

6. If a semicircular sign has a perimeter of 60 inches, find its radius.

1983-C-14

7. *ABCD* is a semicircle in which diameter $AD = 2$ and arc AB = arc CD = 1. Find the length of arc *BC*.

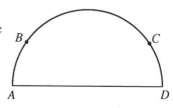

1972-J-7

8. A window consists of a rectangle surmounted by a semicircle. The rectangular portion has a width of 2 feet and a height of 3 feet. Find the perimeter of the window.

1965-J-25

9. If a belt is placed around the equator one foot away from the Earth at all points, how much greater than the circumference of the Earth would the length of the belt be? (Assume that the Earth is a sphere of circumference approximately 25,000 miles.)

1978-J-13

10. AE is divided into four equal parts and semicircles are drawn on AC, CE, AD, and DE, creating paths from A to E as shown. Determine the ratio of the length of the upper path to the length of the lower path.

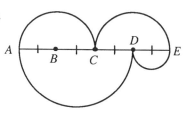

1966-J-23

11. Four rods each of diameter 7 inches are tied together in a bundle with a piece of string. What is the shortest piece of string required for the job, allowing 2 inches extra for tying the knot?

1974-J-22

12. The rear wheel of a carriage has a circumference which is 2 feet more than the circumference of the front wheel. If the front wheel makes 24 more revolutions per mile than the rear wheel, find the circumference of the rear wheel.

1987-C-24

13. A circle is rolled, without slipping, across the top of the other six identical circles to get from position x to position y. Find the number of revolutions it must make.

Wonder Woman gives Superman a five
second head start in a one kilometre race. If
Wonder Woman runs at 5 km per minute and
Superman runs at 3 km per minute, who wins
and by how many metres?

Rates

Multiple Choice Questions

1988-G-9
1. Ann runs at a constant rate on a one-tenth kilometre circular track at the health club.
   She completes a lap in 31 seconds. If she runs at the same rate, the approximate time,
   in minutes, that it takes her to run 8 kilometres is

   (A) 5   (B) 40   (C) 50   (D) 310   (E) 2500

1984-G-22

2. Wonder Woman gives Superman a five second head start in a one km race. If Wonder Woman runs at 5 km per minute and Superman runs at 3 km per minute, the result of the race is

(A) Wonder Woman wins by 3 seconds
(B) Superman wins by 3 seconds
(C) Superman ties Wonder Woman
(D) Wonder Woman wins by 8 seconds
(E) Superman wins by 13 seconds

1978-G-20

3. A motorcycle and a truck left a roadside diner at the same time. After travelling in the same direction for an hour and a quarter the motorcycle had travelled 25 km farther than the truck. If the average speed of the motorcycle was 60 km/h, then the average speed, in km/h, of the truck was

(A) 28   (B) 35   (C) 40   (D) 48   (E) 50

1988-G-15

4. A calendar watch loses one second per day. At this rate, the approximate length of time, in years, for the watch to lose exactly 24 hours is

(A) $\dfrac{1}{360}$ (B) $\dfrac{1}{240}$ (C) 4   (D) 240   (E) 2400

1981-J-13

5. The water in a heating system makes a complete circuit with 26 strokes of the pump. If a complete circuit requires 14 seconds, then the pumping rate in strokes per minute to the nearest integer is

(A) 32   (B) 111   (C) 140   (D) 182   (E) 364

1964-J-13

6. A man travels 100 miles at x miles per hour, 400 miles at $2x$ miles per hour, and 600 miles at $3x$ miles per hour. For the entire trip, his average speed in miles per hour is

(A) 1100   (B) $11x$ (C) $27x$ (D) $2x$ (E) $\dfrac{11x}{5}$

1963-J-18

7. An automobile travels $\dfrac{a}{6}$ feet in r seconds. If this rate is maintained for 3 minutes, how many yards does it travel in the 3 minutes? (note: 1 yard = 3 feet)

(A) $\dfrac{a}{1080r}$ (B) $\dfrac{30r}{a}$ (C) $\dfrac{30a}{r}$ (D) $\dfrac{10r}{a}$ (E) $\dfrac{10a}{r}$

1964-J-14

8. *A* could complete a job in 6 days and *B* could complete the same job in 4 days. Working together they could complete the job in

(A) 10 days   (B) 5 days   (C) 3 days   (D) $\frac{12}{5}$ days   (E) $1\frac{1}{2}$ days

1974-G-25

9. A car is driven up a one-mile long hill at 30 m.p.h., and continues down the other side, which is also one mile in length. The speed the car must be driven on the down slope, in m.p.h., in order to average 60 m.p.h. for the whole trip, is

(A) 30   (B) 90   (C) 60   (D) 120   (E) none of these

1978-J-18

10. A race driver drove one circuit of a six km track. For the first 3 km his speed was 150 km/h, for the next 2 km his speed was 200 km/h, and for the final kilometre his speed was 300 km/h. His average speed for the complete circuit in km/h was

(A) 180   (B) $216\frac{2}{3}$ (C) $191\frac{2}{3}$ (D) 200   (E) none of these

1987-P-23

11. Amy, Brigitte, and Cindy run at constant rates. In a race of 1000 m, Amy finished 200 m ahead of Brigitte and 400 m ahead of Cindy. When Brigitte finished, the number of metres she was ahead of Cindy was

(A) 200   (B) 210   (C) 245   (D) 250   (E) 400

1988-C-22

12. John walks east at a certain rate. Sue starts at the same time from the same place as John and walks south at a rate k times as fast as John's rate. Sue turns and walks directly northeast but John continues to walk east. If Sue eventually meets John, the value of k is

(A) $\sqrt{2}$ (B) $2 + \frac{1}{2}\sqrt{2}$ (C) 3   (D) $2\sqrt{2}$ (E) $\sqrt{2} + 1$

1964-J-31

13. A man makes a trip in $3t$ hours. Two-thirds of the distance travelled was by car and the remainder by boat. If his rate by car was three times his rate by boat, then the number of hours spent in the boat was

(A) $\frac{6}{5}t$ (B) t (C) $\frac{9}{5}t$ (D) $2t$ (E) $\frac{3}{4}t$

1973-J-28

14. Moe and Joe start together at point A and walk towards point B. Moe walks x times as fast as Joe. Moe reaches B, then travels back till he meets Joe. At this point the fraction of the distance AB that Joe has travelled is

(A) $\dfrac{2}{x-1}$ (B) $\dfrac{3}{2x}$ (C) $\dfrac{2}{3+x}$ (D) $\dfrac{3}{1+x}$ (E) $\dfrac{2}{1+x}$

1986-P-23

15. Bette visits her friend Keith and then returns home by the same route. She always walks 2 km/h when going uphill, 6 km/h when going downhill, and 3 km/h when on level ground. If her total walking time is 6 hours, then the total distance she walks, in km, is

(A) 9   (B) 12   (C) 18   (D) 22   (E) 36

1963-J-30

16. Two astronauts Pat and Mike were orbiting the earth in separate space capsules. They were orbiting in the same direction and in the same plane. Pat orbits in 3 hours and Mike in 7.5 hours. At 12 noon Toronto time, Mike sees Pat directly below. The next time that Mike's capsule is directly above Pat's capsule, the the time will be

(A) 4:00 p.m.   (B) 7:30 p.m.   (C) 3:30 p.m.   (D) 5:00 p.m.   (E) 8:00 p.m.

1968-J-29

17. At exactly 12 o'clock, the hour hand of a clock begins to move at twice its normal speed and the minute hand begins to move at half its normal speed. When the two hands next coincide the correct time will be

(A) 1:30   (B) 3:00   (C) 3:30   (D) 4:00   (E) 6:00

Full Solution Questions

1985-G-8

1. A car travels 8 km in five minutes. At this speed, how far would it travel in one hour?

1977-G-26

2. A car travels the 80 miles between Hamilton and London in 2 hours. It continues at the same rate to Windsor, which is 290 miles from Hamilton. What is the total time, in hours, it takes to drive from Hamilton to Windsor?

1975-G-24

3. A train 1000 metres long travels through a 3000 metre tunnel. If 30 seconds elapse from the time the last car enters the tunnel until the time when the engine emerges from the other end, determine the speed, in metres per second, of the train.

1963-J-8

4. A runner takes x steps to run y feet. Determine the number of steps he would take to run one hundred yards. (note: 1 yard = 3 feet)

1975-J-8

5. If a car goes one mile at 30 miles per hour, and then goes another mile at 40 miles per hour, what is its average speed for the 2 miles?

1972-J-14

6. Joe Fireball, in his 1935 Moonbeam Racer, averages 60 mph, 40 mph, and 30 mph on 3 successive runs over a 120 mile course. If he completes the entire 120 miles each time, find his average speed for the three runs.

1980-J-21

7. In a 24 km race, during which each runner maintains a constant speed throughout, A crosses the finish line while B is still 8 km from finishing and C is 12 km from finishing. How many kilometres will C still have to complete when B crosses the finish line?

1963-J-20

8. A bathtub will empty at a uniform rate in 15 minutes. With the plug in, it will fill at a uniform rate in 12 minutes. How long will it take to fill if the plug is removed and the tap turned on?

1989-P-20

9. Constable Nancy is driving along a highway at 100 km/h. She is passed by Pat who is driving in the same direction at a constant speed. Ten seconds after Pat passes Nancy, their cars are 100 m apart. Determine the speed of Pat's car, in km/h.

1979-J-22

10. Frank and Ernest start jogging on a 110 m circular track. They begin at the same time and from the same point but jog in opposite directions, one at $\frac{8}{3}$ m per second and the other at $\frac{7}{3}$ m per second. How many times will they meet during the first 15 minutes of jogging?

1974-J-24

11. Every hour on the hour, beginning at midnight, a train leaves Toronto for Montreal, and at the same time a train leaves Montreal for Toronto. The distance from Toronto to Montreal is 301 miles, and every train travels at 60 miles per hour. How many trains will a train departing from Toronto at 7 a.m. meet on its run to Montreal?

1965-J-28

12. A man walked from *A* to *B* at 4 mph and from *B* to *C* at 3 mph. Then he walked from *C* to *B* at 6 mph and from *B* to *A* at 4 mph. If the total time taken for the walk was 6 hours and *AB* ≠ *BC*, how far did he walk altogether?

1966-J-26

13. Two candles of the same height are lit at the same time. The first is consumed in four hours, the second in three hours. Assuming that each candle burns at a constant rate, how many hours after being lit was the first candle twice the height of the second?

1966-J-27

14. A man has walked two-thirds of the distance across a railroad bridge when he observes a train approaching at 45 miles per hour. What must his rate of speed be if he can just manage to escape by running at the same uniform speed to either end of the bridge?

1977-J-23

15. The visibility at sea, on a certain day, is 5 miles. Ships *A* and *B* are travelling in opposite directions on courses which are parallel and 3 miles apart. The two ships are in sight of one another for 24 minutes. If ship *A* is travelling at 8 mph, how fast is ship *B* travelling?

1975-J-30

16. Two trucks left two towns *A* and *B* at the same time, and each was driven to the other town at a constant speed, passing each other at point *C*. The truck from *B* completed the journey from *C* to *A* in 20 minutes. The truck from *A* completed the journey from *C* to *B* in 45 minutes, while maintaining its steady speed of 40 mph. Find the speed of the other truck in miles per hour.

Five yeast cells were placed in a laboratory dish at 4 p.m. If the number of yeast cells doubles in every ten-minute interval, what is the number of cells in the dish at the end of one hour?

Sequences and Series

Multiple Choice Questions

1975-G-25
1. A sequence is 2, 3, 5, 9, 17, ... A possible sixth number in this sequence is

(A) 65   (B) 35   (C) 67   (D) 21   (E) 33

1979-G-10
2. Starting at 13 and counting by 8s, a student counts 13, 21, etc. A number that will be counted is

(A) 34   (B) 48   (C) 53   (D) 63   (E) 71

1977-G-14

3. If the number pattern shown is continued, then the second number in the fifteenth row is

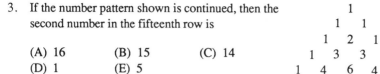

(A) 16   (B) 15   (C) 14

(D) 1   (E) 5

1985-C-11

4. The integers greater than 1 are arranged, four in each row, in five columns as follows:

a	b	c	d	e
2	3	4	5	
	9	8	7	6
10	11	12	13	
	17	16	15	14

If the pattern is followed, the number 1000 will occur in column

(A) a (B) b (C) c (D) d (E) e

1983-G-21

5. Starting at 777 and counting backwards by 7s, a student counts 777, 770, 763, etc. A number that will be counted is

(A) 45   (B) 44   (C) 43   (D) 42   (E) 41

1973-J-15

6. The sum of the first n even positive integers is p and the sum of the first n odd positive integers is q. Then $p - q$ is equal to

(A) 1   (B) n (C) $-n$ (D) $\frac{n}{2}$ (E) $\frac{n}{2} - 1$

1980-J-22

7. The numbers 2, 5, 8, 11, 14, ... (where each number is three greater than the one preceding it) are written in order in a book, one hundred to a page, beginning on page one. The number 11 111 will be found on page

(A) 37   (B) 38   (C) 39   (D) 40   (E) 41

1983-G-16

8. Five yeast cells were placed in a laboratory dish at 4 p.m. The number of yeast cells doubles in every ten minute interval. At the end of one hour the number of cells in the dish will be

(A) 320   (B) 640   (C) 64   (D) 15 625   (E) 160

1987-C-6

9. In the sequence 5, 16, 27, …, each term is 11 greater than the preceding term. A term in this sequence is

(A) 90   (B) 91   (C) 92   (D) 93   (E) 94

1988-P-18

10. In a sequence of six numbers, the first number is 4 and the last number is 47. Each number after the second equals the sum of the previous two numbers. If S is the sum of the six numbers in this sequence, then S lies in the interval

(A) 51 to 90   (B) 91 to 100   C) 101 to 110
(D) 111 to 120   (E) 121 to 160

1985-G7-21

11. The interior of circle A contains only the whole numbers from 1 to 50. Circle B contains only the odd numbers from 1 to 50. Circle C contains only the multiples of 7 from 1 to 50. The number of numbers in the shaded area is

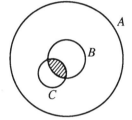

(A) 7   (B) 5   (C) 4
(D) 3   (E) 1

1989-P-14

12. The largest four-digit number to be found in the arithmetic sequence 1, 4, 7, 10, 13, 16, … is

(A) 9995   (B) 9996   (C) 9997   (D) 9998   (E) 9999

1987-F-17

13. The sum of fifty consecutive even integers is 3250. The largest of these integers is

(A) 65   (B) 66   (C) 112   (D) 114   (E) 116

1984-P-25

14. If $1 + \dfrac{1}{2^2} + \dfrac{1}{3^2} + \dfrac{1}{4^2} + \dfrac{1}{5^2} + \ldots = x$, then the value of

$$1 + \frac{1}{2^2} + \frac{1}{4^2} + \frac{1}{6^2} + \frac{1}{8^2} + \ldots \text{ is}$$

(A) $\dfrac{x}{2}$ (B) $\dfrac{x}{2} - 1$ (C) $\dfrac{x}{4} + 1$ (D) 2   (E) $\dfrac{x}{4} - 1$

1970-J-30

15. An arithmetic sequence is a set of numbers of the form
$$a, a + d, a + 2d, a + 3d, \ldots$$
If the kth term of an arithmetic sequence is equal to m, and the mth term is equal to k, then the nth term is

(A) $k + m - n$ (B) $n - k - m$ (C) $n - k + m$

(D) n (E) $k - m - n$

1982-P-24

16. The sum of the first n natural numbers is $\dfrac{n(n + 1)}{2}$. The sum of the natural numbers, between 1 and 4000 inclusive, which are *not* multiples of 5 is

(A) 7 681 600   (B) 1 602 000   (C) 8 002 000   (D) 8 000 000   (E) 6 400 000

1988-G-20

17. January 1, 1986 occurred on a Wednesday. January 1, 1992 will occur on a

(A) Tuesday   (B) Wednesday   (C) Thursday   (D) Friday   (E) Saturday

1989-C-24

18. The sum $1^4 + 2^4 + 3^4 + 4^4 + \ldots + n^4$ is given by the expression $\dfrac{6n^5 + an^4 + bn^3 - n}{30}$. The value of $a - b$ is

(A) -25 (B) -15 (C) -5 (D) 5   (E) 25

1978-J-25

19. The multiples of 2 and 5 are removed from the set of positive integers
$1, 2, 3, \ldots, 10n$, n an integer. The sum of the remaining integers is

(A) $10n^3 - 40n^2 + 110n - 60$ (B) $30n^2 - 30n + 20$ (C) $15n^2 + 5n$

(D) $20n^2$ (E) none of these

1985-F-22

20. If $f(n) = 1 + \dfrac{1}{2} + \dfrac{1}{3} + \dfrac{1}{4} + \ldots + \dfrac{1}{n}$, then the value of $f(60) - f(40)$ lies between

(A) 0.1 and 0.3   (B) 0.3 and 0.5   (C) 0.5 and 0.7   (D) 0.7 and 0.9   (E) 0.9 and 1.1

Full Solution Questions

1985-G7-16

1. Triangular numbers follow this pattern:

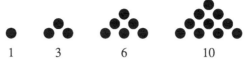

1   3   6   10

The first four triangular numbers are 1, 3, 6, and 10. What is the seventh triangular number?

1985-G-10

2. If the pattern shown is continued, how many letters will appear in the "K" column?

1974-G-23

3. A sequence is 1, 2, 5, 10, 17, ... What is the seventh number in this sequence?

1986-G7-11

4. The numbers in the sequence 2, 7, 12, 22, ... increase by fives. The numbers in the sequence 3, 10, 17, 24, 31, ... increase by sevens. The number 17 occurs in *both* sequences. What is the next number which occurs in *both* sequences?

1982-G-11

5. Starting at 7 and counting by 13s, a student counts 7, 20, 33, etc. Explain why the number 72 will be counted.

1974-G-21

6. What is the sum of the odd integers from 1 to 99, including 1 and 99?

1981-G-22

7. A base row of blocks is formed and rows of blocks are added so that each new row has one fewer block than the row below it. If the base has nine blocks and the final row has one block, what is the total number of blocks used?

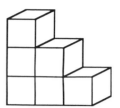

1968-J-25

8. The positive integers are arranged in the pattern indicated in the diagram. What number will be found in the square for the 61st (horizontal) row and 23rd (vertical) column?

1				
2	3			
4	5	6		
7	8	9	10	
11	12	13	14	15

1986-G8-11

9. When Karl Friedrich Gauss was a young lad he discovered that the sum, S, of the first n natural numbers is given by the formula

$$S = \frac{n(n + 1)}{2}.$$

What is the sum of the first 30 natural numbers?

1986-G8-9

10. My rich uncle gave me one dollar for my first birthday. On each birthday after that, he doubled his previous gift. Find the total amount that he had given me by the day after my eighth birthday.

1967-J-11

11. At exactly one o'clock two friendly bacteria were placed in a medium. One minute later there were four bacteria. In another minute there were eight bacteria, etc. At exactly two o'clock there was one gallon of bacteria. At what time was there one quart of bacteria?

1987-P-12

12. What is the 1987th term in the sequence
$$-2, -1, 0, 1, 2, -2, -1, 0, 1, 2, -2, -1, 0, 1, 2, \ldots ?$$

1988-P-4

13. If the 24th day of June is on Thursday, what day of the week was the first day of June in the same year?

1988-G-8

14. One plant is now 12 cm tall and will grow 2 cm per week. A second plant is now 3 cm tall and will grow 5 cm per week. How many weeks does it take before the plants are the same height?

1988-G-8

15. While waiting for the school bus, Sally plays a counting game. After taking two steps forward, she must take one step backward. She wishes to reach a tree which is seven steps away from her. Using this rule, what is the least number of steps she must take to reach the tree?

1985-P-21

16. What is the least number of consecutive positive integers, that add up to 1000?

1979-J-27

17. The sum of the first sixty terms of the series
$$\frac{1}{(2)(3)} + \frac{1}{(3)(4)} + \frac{1}{(4)(5)} + \dots + \frac{1}{(n+1)(n+2)} + \dots \text{ is } \frac{a}{b},$$
where a and b are relatively prime integers. What is the value of $a + b$?

1987-F-20

18. If $f(3) = 1$ and $f(3n) = n + f(3n - 3)$, where n is any integer greater than 1, determine the value of $f(21)$.

1975-J-25

19. If $f(n + 1) = \frac{2f(n) + 1}{2}$ and $f(1) = 1$, find $f(235)$.

A soup bowl in the shape of a hemisphere of diameter 16 cm is filled to half its depth. What is the maximum angle through which the bowl may be tilted without spilling any soup?

3-Dimensional Problems

Multiple Choice Questions

1986-G7-20

1. The figure below which can be obtained by rotating the figure on the right is

(A) 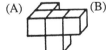　(B) 　(C) 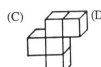　(D) 　(E)

1985-G7-19

2. The sides of a cube are doubled in length to form a larger cube. The number of original small cubes that will fill this larger cube is

    (A) 2   (B) 4   (C) 6   (D) 8   (E) 16

1973-J-8

3. A rectangular $4 \times 3 \times 2$ block has its surface painted red, and then is cut into cubes with each edge 1 unit. The number of cubes having exactly one of its faces painted red is

    (A) 0   (B) 4   (C) 8   (D) 12   (E) 24

1986-C-23

4. A polyhedron P has for its vertices the midpoints of each edge of a rectangular block. The sum of the number of edges and the number of faces of P is

    (A) 46   (B) 38   (C) 36   (D) 18   (E) none of these

1984-C-15

5. A cylindrical pail with diameter 26 cm is filled with water to a depth of 30 cm. The entire contents of the pail are then poured into an empty rectangular fish tank which has base dimensions 52 cm by 39 cm. If the tank has vertical sides then the water will attain a depth, in centimetres, of

    (A) $\frac{5}{13}\pi$ (B) $\frac{5}{2}\pi$ (C) 10π (D) $\frac{195}{7}\pi$ (E) none of these

1979-J-25

6. A soup bowl in the shape of a hemisphere of diameter 16 cm is filled to half its depth. The maximum angle through which the bowl may be tilted without spilling any soup is

    (A) $22\frac{1}{2}^{\circ}$ (B) 30° (C) 45° (D) 60° (E) $67\frac{1}{2}^{\circ}$

1980-J-26

7. A clear plastic cube of edge 1 unit has within it a blue regular octahedron, each of whose vertices is the midpoint of one of the faces of the cube. The volume of the octahedron, in cubic units, is

    (A) $\frac{1}{2}$ (B) $\frac{1}{3}$ (C) $\frac{1}{4}$ (D) $\frac{1}{6}$ (E) $\frac{1}{8}$

1964-J-27

8. The volume of a sphere of radius r is $\frac{4}{3}\pi r^3$. If a spherical balloon is inflated so that its radius is doubled, then the volume is increased by a factor of

(A) 2   (B) 4   (C) 6   (D) 8   (E) 16

1968-J-18

9. The tip of a straight reed growing in the centre of a pond 8 feet in diameter reaches one foot above the water. When the reed is pulled over, with its bottom fixed, the tip can just be made to touch the edge of the pond. The depth of the pond, in feet, at the centre is

(A) $\frac{15}{2}$ (B) 4   (C) 3   (D) 8   (E) $\sqrt{17}$

1967-J-24

10. An ant wishes to travel from A to B on the surface of a wooden block with dimensions $2 \times 4 \times 8$ as shown. The shortest distance it can walk is

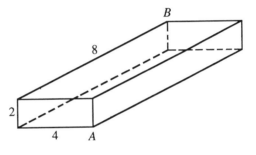

(A) 14   (B) $2 + \sqrt{80}$
(C) $8 + \sqrt{20}$ (D) $4 + \sqrt{68}$
(E) 10

1982-F-23

11. A coil of very thin wire with one end attached to the edge of the base of a hollow cylinder of radius 5 cm and height 10 cm is to be wound without overlap exactly 10 times around the cylinder so that the other end is attached to the edge of the top. The shortest length of wire required, in centimetres, is

(A) $10\sqrt{1 + 100\pi^2}$ (B) $10 + 100\pi$ (C) 100π
(D) $10\sqrt{1 + \pi^2}$ (E) $100\sqrt{1 + \pi^2}$

1973-J-14

12. If each edge of a cube is increased by 150%, the percentage increase in the surface area is

(A) 125   (B) 225   (C) 525   (D) 625   (E) none of these

1969-J-17

13. A rectangular box has dimensions r, s, and t units, where $r < s < t$. If one dimension only is increased by one unit, then the increase in volume

  (A) is greatest when r is increased
  (B) is greatest when s is increased
  (C) is greatest when t is increased
  (D) is the same regardless of which dimension is increased
  (E) cannot be determined from the information given.

1983-F-22

14. The volume of the cone in the diagram is
$\frac{1}{3}$(area of base)(height) $= \frac{1}{3}Ah$.
The top is removed by slicing with a plane parallel to the base plane, and distance $\frac{2}{3}h$ from it. The volume remaining is

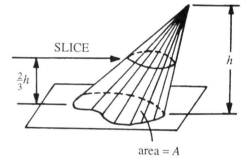
SLICE
$\frac{2}{3}h$
h
area $= A$

  (A) $\frac{8}{81}Ah$ (B) $\frac{26}{27}Ah$

  (C) $\frac{8}{27}Ah$ (D) $\frac{2}{9}Ah$

  (E) $\frac{26}{81}Ah$

1988-G-16

15. Three cuts are made through a large cube to make eight identical smaller cubes. The total surface area of the smaller cubes is

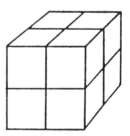

  (A) one-eighth of the surface area of the larger cube
  (B) one-half of the surface area of the larger cube
  (C) double the surface area of the larger cube
  (D) eight times the surface area of the larger cube
  (E) the same as the surface area of the larger cube

1988-G-24

16. Each of the numbers 1, 2, 3, 4, 5, 6 is painted, one to a face, on the faces of a cube. The cube is placed on a table so that from each of three positions a person can see the top and two other faces. The sums of numbers showing on the visible faces from the three positions are 9, 14, and 15. The number on the bottom face is

  (A) 1   (B) 2   (C) 3   (D) 4   (E) 5

Full Solution Questions

1984-G-7
1. How many edges are there on a triangular-based prism?

1979-G-23
2. A $3 \times 3 \times 3$ cube is painted red and is then cut into 27 unit cubes. How many of these small cubes will have paint on exactly two faces?

1987-P-25
3. The surface of a cube is to be painted so that no two faces of the same colour share a common edge. What is the minimum number of different colours required to paint the cube?

4. A rectangular box has dimensions 9 cm by 6 cm by 24 cm. A second rectangular box has volume one half of the first and has a base 6 cm by 4 cm. What is the height of the box?

1985-C-24
5. A paper cone, when cut along its slant height S, and opened out, forms a semi-circle of radius 10 cm. Find the height h of the cone

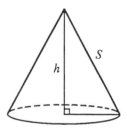

1964-J-17
6. The lengths, in inches, of the three edges meeting at each corner of a rectangular box are 1, 2, and 3. What is the length of the diagonal of this box ?

1982-F-21
7. A cube rests inside a sphere so that each vertex touches the sphere. Find the volume of the cube, if the inner radius of the sphere is 6 cm.

1965-J-24
8. A rectangular container with base 9 cm by 11 cm has a height is 38.5 cm. Assuming that water expands 10% when it freezes, determine the depth to which the container can be filled so that when the contents freeze the ice does not go above the edge of the container.

1966-J-18

9. A rectangular tank with base a square of side 4 feet contains water to a height of 3 feet. A solid cube of edge 2 feet is placed on the bottom of the tank. What is the new height of the water?

1967-J-16

10. An open box is made from a square piece of tin by removing a 6 inch square from each corner and turning up the sides. If the volume of the box is 864 cubic inches find the area of the original square.

1988-P-21

11. An open box is constructed by gluing a number of 1 cm cubes together to form the bottom and the sides. The outside dimensions of the finished box are 10 cm by 10 cm by 10 cm, and the sides and bottom are all 1 cm thick. Determine the number of cubes required to construct the box.

1987-P-22

12. A fish tank, filled with water, is 100 cm long, 60 cm wide, and 40 cm high. It is tilted, as shown, resting on a 60 cm edge, with the water level reaching C, the midpoint of AB. Find the depth of water in the fish tank once AB is returned to a horizontal position.

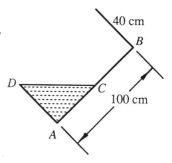

1986-P-24

13. A cube having an edge length of 10 is sliced into two sections by a cut in the plane of ABC, as shown in the diagram. Find the volume of the smaller section.

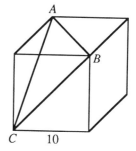

1981-J-27

14. Three spheres of diameter 2 are placed on a level surface so that each sphere touches the other two. A fourth sphere, also of diameter 2, is placed on top of the other three so that it touches all of the other spheres. Find the distance from the level surface to the highest point of the top sphere.

1987-C-25

15. A cylindrical tank with a diameter of 120 cm and a height of 400 cm is open at the top and is filled with water to a height of 200 cm. A solid cone with a diameter of 60 cm and a height of 100 cm is suspended, vertex up, above the water so that the base of the cone just touches the surface of the water. The cone is then lowered into the water until it is just covered. How far has the cone been lowered?

1977-J-22

16. A cylindrical gasoline storage tank, lying on its side, has an inside diameter of 4 feet and an inside length of 16 feet. If the depth of the gasoline is 3 feet, find the area of the top surface of the gasoline in the tank.

1989-P-21

17. A cuboctohedron is a polyhedron formed by slicing a cube at the midpoints of its edges as shown. Determine the surface area of a cubctohedron formed from a cube having each edge of length 4.

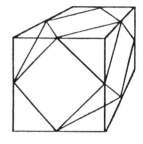

It requires 3 litres of paint to cover a floor. If each dimension of the floor is doubled, how many litres are required to cover the floor with the same thickness of paint?

Rectilinear Figures

Multiple Choice Questions

1986-P-2

1. A triangle has sides of length 6, 10, and 11. An equilateral triangle has the same perimeter. The length of each side of the equilateral triangle is

    (A) 6   (B) 9   (C) 10   (D) 11   (E) 27

1968-J-5

2. In the figure, 15 rectangles, each of height h and width w, are shown. The perimeter of the figure formed is

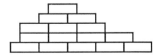

    (A) $15w + 15h$ (B) $10w + 10h$
    (C) $30w + 15h$ (D) $30w + 30h$
    (E) none of these

3. The area of a rectangle is A and the length is L. The perimeter of the rectangle is

   (A) $2L + 2A$ (B) $2L + \dfrac{A}{L}$ (C) $2L + \dfrac{A}{2L}$ (D) $2L + \dfrac{2A}{L}$ (E) none of these

1984-P-4
4. The area of the given figure is

   (A) 45   (B) 35   (C) 41
   (D) 32   (E) 62

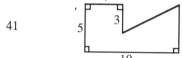

1977-J-6
5. The area of pentagon $ABCDE$ is

   (A) 120   (B) 72   (C) 48
   (D) 96   (E) 108

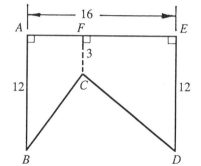

1985-P-11
6. A rectangle is 24 cm long and 15 cm wide. Its length is decreased by 6 cm. To keep the same area, its width, in centimetres, must be increased by

   (A) 3   (B) 5   (C) 6   (D) 20   (E) 21

1982-P-15
7. The sides of a right-angled triangle are 15 cm, 20 cm, and 25 cm. The length, in centimetres, of the altitude drawn to the longest side is

   (A) 12.5   (B) 12   (C) $\dfrac{15}{2}\sqrt{2}$ (D) 9   (E) $10\sqrt{2}$

1971-J-26
8. A rhombus is formed by two radii and two chords of a circle whose radius is 8. The area of the rhombus is

   (A) 32   (B) $32\sqrt{3}$ (C) 64   (D) 128   (E) $128\sqrt{3}$

1984-P-13

9. A rectangular box has dimensions 9 cm by 6 cm by 24 cm. A second rectangular box
    has volume one-half of the first and has a base 6 cm by 4 cm. The height of the box,
    in centimetres, is

    (A) 12   (B) 16   (C) 27   (D) 54   (E) 108

1964-J-26

10. A square of side $2x$ has four equilateral triangles drawn on its sides (and exterior to
    the square). The area of the figure formed is

    (A) $4(1 + \sqrt{3})x^2$ (B) $\dfrac{(1 + \sqrt{3})x^2}{4}$ (C) $(4 + \sqrt{3})x^2$ (D) $(1 + 4\sqrt{3})x^2$ (E) none of these

1966-J-28

11. A circular piece of metal of maximum size is cut from a square piece, and then a square
    piece of maximum size is cut from the circular piece. The total amount of metal wasted
    is

    (A) $\dfrac{1}{4}$ the area of the original square   (B) $\dfrac{1}{2}$ the area of the original square

    (C) $\dfrac{1}{2}$ the area of the circular piece   (D) $\dfrac{1}{4}$ the area of the circular piece

    (E) none of these

1970-J-14

12. In the accompanying diagram, all lines which meet
    do so at right angles. If the area of the figure is 60
    square units, and if $3 < x < 5$, then

    (A) $1.5 < h < 5.5$ (B) $3.5 < h < 8.5$
    (C) $6 < h < 10$ (D) $12 < h < 20$
    (E) $7.5 < h < 16.5$

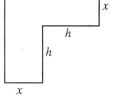

1988-G8-11

13. A square piece of paper is folded in half to form a rectangle. This rectangle has a
    perimeter of 18 cm. The area of the original square, in cm^2, was

    (A) 9   (B) 12   (C) 18   (D) 24   (E) 36

1970-J-23

14. The perimeter of a rectangle is x inches. If the ratio of two adjacent sides is $a : b$,
    ($a > b$), then the length of the shorter side, in inches, is

    (A) $\dfrac{bx}{a + b}$ (B) $\dfrac{x}{2} - a$ (C) $\dfrac{2bx}{a + b}$ (D) $\dfrac{ax}{2(a + b)}$ (E) $\dfrac{bx}{2(a + b)}$

15. *ABCD* is a rectangle with $AD = 6$ and $AB = 12$.
    $DF \parallel EB$ and $EG \perp DF$. If the area of *DEBF* is
    12, then the length of *EG* is

    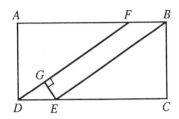

    (A) $\frac{3\sqrt{34}}{17}$ (B) $\frac{3\sqrt{34}}{34}$ (C) $\frac{3}{2}$

    (D) 2   (E) none of these

16. A 3-metre square and a 4-metre square overlap as
    shown in the diagram. *D* is the centre of the
    3-metre square. The area of the shaded region
    DEFG, in square metres, is

    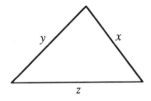

    (A) 2.00   (B) 2.25   (C) 2.50

    (D) 3.00   (E) 1.75

1975-J-15

17. If the area of the triangle is *A*, and $x < y < z$,
    then the shortest altitude is

    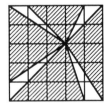

    (A) $\frac{A}{2x}$ (B) $\frac{2A}{x}$ (C) $\frac{A}{2z}$

    (D) $\frac{2A}{z}$ (E) none of these

18. In the diagram, drawn on the square grid, the ratio
    of the shaded area to the unshaded area is

    (A) 4:1   (B) 5:1   (C) 6:1

    (D) 21:4   (E) 25:4

19. The lengths of the sides of a right-angled triangle are $2x - 5$, $2x + 2$, and $2x + 3$.
    The area of the triangle is

    (A) $2x^2 + 5x + 3$ (B) $4x^2 - 6x - 10$ (C) $2x^2 - 3x - 5$

    (D) $2x^2 + 4x + 2$ (E) $4x^2 + 12x + 19$

1984-F-21
20. The area of trapezoid *ABCD* is 18 square units,
    AB = 4 units, and *DE* = $\frac{1}{4}$*DC*. If the altitude of
    the trapezoid is an integer and the side *DC* is an odd
    integer, then the area of triangle *ABE* is

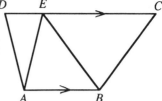

(A) 9   (B) 6   (C) $\frac{18}{5}$

(D) 8   (E) none of these

1988-F-15
21. If *AP* = *EP* = *DQ* = *FQ* = 1 and the area of
    rectangle *ABCD* is equal to the area of the square
    EFGH, then *BC* is equal to

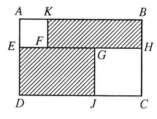

(A) 2   (B) 2 + $\sqrt{2}$ (C) 4

(D) 2 + $\sqrt{7}$ (E) 5

1988-P-16
22. A rectangle *ABCD* has a square *AEFK* of area 4,
    and a square *GHCJ* of area 9 removed. If *EFGH*
    is a straight line segment and *FG* = 5, then the total
    area of the two shaded rectangles is

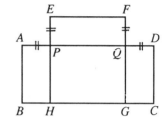

(A) 31   (B) 33   (C) 35

(D) 37   (E) 40

1989-C-5
23. The perimeter of a rectangle is 2*y* + 4 and the length is *y*. The area of the rectangle is

(A) 2*y*   (B) y^2 + 2*y*   (C) 4*y*   (D) 4y^2 (E) y^2 + 4*y*

1988-G7-23
24. The dots are one unit apart, horizontally and
    vertically. The area, in square units, of the figure
    shown is

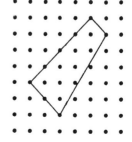

(A) 8   (B) 9$\frac{1}{2}$ (C) 10

(D) 10$\frac{1}{2}$ (E) 12

1988-C-21

25. In rectangle $ABCD$, $AD = 10$, and $AB = 8$. Point K is chosen in DC such that, when triangle ADK is reflected in AK, the image of D is on BC. The length of DK is

    (A) 5   (B) 6   (C) $2\sqrt{2}$ (D) $3\sqrt{3}$ (E) $4\sqrt{2}$

Full Solution Questions

1983-P-12

1. In the dotted rectangle $PQRS$, sides $RS = 16$ and $QR = 12$. If all angles in the diagram are right angles, what is the length of the solid-line path from P to Q?

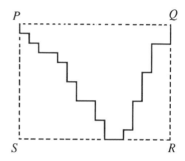

1989-P-8

2. $ABCD$ is a square with E on DC such that $DE = 2$ and $EC = 4$. Calculate the area of $\triangle AEB$.

1985-P-6

3. The figure shown is formed using square tiles. If each side of a tile is one unit in length, what is the perimeter of the figure?

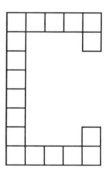

1988-G8-17

4. Each of the equal sides of an isosceles triangle is 5 cm longer than the third side. The perimeter of the triangle is 31 cm. Determine the length of each equal side.

1988-P-6

5. It requires 3 litres of paint to cover a floor. If each dimension of the floor is doubled, determine the number of litres required to cover the floor with the same thickness of paint.

1988-G8-10

6. Each visible face of a block in the pile shown measures 2 cm by 8 cm. Determine the length of the path marked with solid line segments.

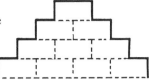

1976-J-6

7. What is the area of figure *ABCD*?

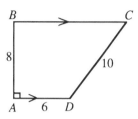

1979-J-9

8. Find the area of *ABCDE*.

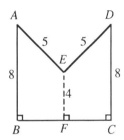

1971-J-8

9. A square of side $2n + 1$ has another square of side $2n$ inside it. What is the area between the two squares?

1978-J-7

10. Find the perimeter of the figure shown, given that its area is 108.

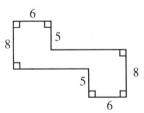

1980-J-14

11. A wire 60 cm in length is cut into two parts in the ratio 2 : 1. Each part is bent to form a square. What is the total area of the two squares?

1985-F-11

12. Find the length of the path
    down the middle of the
    corridor as shown.

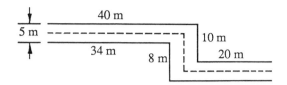

1965-J-14

13. The area of triangle *ABC* is 24 square inches.
    XAY is parallel to *BC*; *AD* = 6 inches; *XY* = 20
    inches. Find the area of figure *BXYC*.

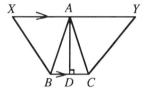

1984-P-18

14. The area of triangle *ABC* is 12 and the height from *A* is an odd integer greater than 1.
    If the base *BC* is an integer, find its length .

1965-J-20

15. *P*, *A*, *B*, and *Q* are collinear points with *A* between *P* and *B*, and with *B* between
    A and *Q*. *PA*, *AB*, and *BQ* are the sides of squares having areas 100, 16, and 81
    square units respectively. By how much must the area of the square on *AB* be
    decreased in order that the total length *PQ* of the sides of the resulting three squares be
    21 units?

1975-J-19

16. *ABCD* is a parallelogram in which *AP* = 12,
    DQ = 16, *CS* = 10, *PQ* = 5, and *QR* = 2. Find
    the area of figure *BRSC*.

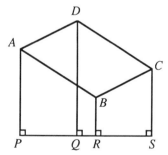

1963-J-9

17. A calendar *h* inches long is designed with a picture *a* inches by *b* inches and a
    calendar pad *c* inches by *d* inches. The picture and the pad together take up one-half
    the area of the calendar. Find the width of the calendar.

1967-J-15

18. The base of a triangle is four times as long as a side of a square. If the triangle and the square have equal areas, find the ratio of the altitude of the triangle to a side of the square.

1971-J-21

19. Find the area of triangle *ADE* in the diagram.

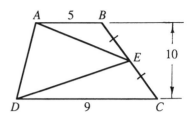

1982-F-11

20. *ABCD* is a square of side 12. Points *E, F,* and *G* are taken on *BC, CD,* and *DA* respectively so that *BE* : *BC* = 1 : 4, *DF* : *DC* = 1 : 3, and *AG* : *AD* = 1 : 2. Find the area of triangle *GEF*.

1985-F-15

21. A triangle has sides of length *x, y,* and *z,* with $x < y < z$. If the length of the shortest altitude is h. Find the length of the longest altitude.

1976-J-21

22. How many scalene triangles exist which have all sides of integral length and a perimeter less than 13?

1988-F-8

23. Rectangle *WXYZ* has length 12 and width 9. Points *A* and *B* divide *WX* into three equal parts. Similarly, *C* and *D* do the same to *XY*, *E* and *F* to *YZ*, and *G* and *H* to *ZW*. Determine the perimeter of the octagon formed by these eight points.

1988-F-17

24. *BAC* and *CDB* are overlapping triangles, each with sides 3, 4, and 5. If *BC* is 5, determine the area common to the two triangles.

1989-P-22

25. In the diagram, the lengths of all line
    segments are integers and all angles are
    right angles. The area of rectangle *ABIH*
    is 6 and the area of rectangle *IDEF* is 15.
    Determine the largest possible area for
    rectangle *ACEG*.

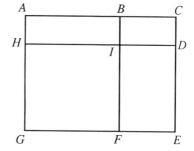

The odometer on a car reads 2722 km. What is the least number of kilometres that must be travelled before the odometer will again show a number in which three digits are the same?

Number Theory

Multiple Choice Questions

1976-J-5
1. The digits of the number 4193 are arranged in descending order and then in ascending order. The difference between the resulting numbers is

    (A) 7902   (B) 8082   (C) 8092   (D) 6174   (E) 0279

1986-C-7
2. Consider the set of 4-digit positive integers where each integer is composed of four different digits. When the smallest number in the set is subtracted from the largest, the result is

    (A) 8888   (B) 8876   (C) 8853   (D) 8646   (E) 8642

1983-P-3

3. The odometer on a car reads 2722 km. The least number of kilometres that must be travelled before the odometer will again show a number in which three digits are the same is between

    (A) 0 and 50   (B) 50 and 100   (C) 100 and 500
    (D) 500 and 1000   (E) 1000 and 5000

1982-G-6

4. $3 \times 10^5 + 4 \times 10^3 + 7 \times 10^2 + 5$ is equal to

    (A) 304 705   (B) 347 500   (C) $3\,475 \times 10^{10}$
    (D) 30 000 040 007 005   (E) 3 475

1982-G-15

5. Each letter in the subtraction that follows represents a single digit.

    $$\begin{array}{cccc} 6 & p & q & r \\ k & 3 & 5 & 9 \\ \hline 1 & 5 & 8 & 8 \end{array}$$

    The letters k, p, q, r in order are

    (A) 4, 3, 9, 7   (B) 5, 9, 4, 7   (C) 5, 3, 9, 7   (D) 5, 1, 3, 7   (E) 4, 5, 0, 7

1978-J-9

6. If the digit 1 is placed between the digits of a two digit number whose tens digit is t and whose units digit is u, then the new number equals

    (A) $10t + 1 + u$ (B) $t + 1 + u$ (C) $10t + 10 + u$
    (D) $100t + 10 + u$ (E) $100t + 1 + u$

1963-J-21

7. In our number system the base is ten. If the base was changed to four, you would count as follows: 1, 2, 3, 10, 11, 12, 13, 20, 21, 22, 23, 30,.... . Then the twentieth number would be

    (A) 20   (B) 38   (C) 44   (D) 104   (E) 110

1987-P-24

8. Consider the set of 3-digit positive numbers, in which none of the digits is zero. If the order of the digits in any number of the set is reversed and the non-negative difference between this number and the original number is x, then the number of possible values of x is

    (A) 8   (B) 9   (C) 10   (D) 45   (E) more than 50

1983-P-20
9. If the 4-digit number 8*mn*9 is a perfect square, then *m* + *n* is

(A) 1   (B) 5   (C) 9   (D) 10   (E) 11

1988-C-19
10. The digits 1, 2, 3, 4, and 5 are each used once to compose a five digit number *abcde*, such that the three digit number *abc* is divisible by 4, *bcd* is divisible by 5, and *cde* is divisible by 3. The digit *a* is

(A) 1   (B) 2   (C) 3   (D) 4   (E) 5

1989-C-14
11. Each of the numbers 1, 9, 8, and 9 is represented by one of the letters *A, B, D*, and *M* (not necessarily in that order). The largest possible sum of the three 3-digit numbers *BAD, DAM*, and *MAD* is

(A) 2159   (B) 2655   (C) 2656   (D) 2657   (E) 2958

1988-G-25
12. The number of integers between 100 and 1000 such that the sum of their digits is 10 is

(A) 36   (B) 54   (C) 55   (D) 62   (E) 63

Full Solution Questions

1985-G7-9
1. The digits of the number 4795 can be rearranged to form different numbers. What is the sum of the largest and smallest of these numbers?

1984-G-17
2. In the product shown at the right, the letters *P* and *Q* represent different digits from 1 to 9. Find *P* and *Q*.

$$\begin{array}{r} P\,8 \\ 3Q \\ \hline 2730 \end{array}$$

1964-J-29
3. Our number system has base 10 and uses the digits 0 to 9 inclusive. A number system with base 8 uses the 8 digits 0 to 7 inclusive. If 267 and 135 are numbers in the system using base 8, find their sum using base 8.

1965-J-17

4. The Martians use a number system which has five digits. Their numbers are 0, 1, 2, 3, 4, 10, 11, 12, 13, 14, 20, etc. Uncle Martin buys a car for 11 000 Martian dollars. He is allowed 3 124 Martian dollars for his old car on a trade-in. Determine the number of Martian dollars he must pay to make up the difference between cost and trade-in allowance.

1976-G-23

5. A palindrome is a number which remains the same when its digits are written in reverse order. For example, 131 is a palindrome. A car's odometer reads 15 951. What is the least number of kilometres that must be driven for the next palindrome to appear?

1988-C-12

6. Determine the number of integers between 500 and 600 which have 12 as the sum of their digits.

1988-P-23

7. The digits 1, 2, 3, 4, 5, and 6 are each used once to compose a six digit number *abcdef*, such that the three digit number *abc* is divisible by 4, *bcd* is divisible by 5 and *cde* is divisible by 3, and *def* is divisible by 11. Determine all possible assignments of the digits to the letters.

1988-G -21

8. The digits used to number the pages of a book were counted, and the total number of digits used was 216. Determine the number of pages in the book.

1989-F-24

9. When a positive number N is expressed in base 9, it has three digits. When N is expressed in base 6 it has the same digits, but in reverse order. Determine the middle digit of these three digits.

1989-F-22

10. N is a positive integer whose units digit is 4. If the 4 is moved to the front of the number a new integer M is formed which is four times N. Determine the number of digits in the smallest N that satisfies the condition.

1977-J-25

11. X and Y are positive integers. The sum of the digits of X is 53, and the sum of the digits of Y is 47. If the addition of X and Y involves exactly 5 carries, find the sum of the digits of $X + Y$.

1987-C-23

12. A four-digit number which is a perfect square is created by writing Anne's age in years followed by Tom's age in years. Similarly, in 31 years, their ages in the same order will again form a four-digit perfect square. Determine the present ages of Anne and Tom.

If a 3 metre stake casts a shadow 7 metres long, what is the height of a tree, in metres, that casts a shadow 63 metres long?

Similar Triangles

Multiple Choice Questions

1963-J-6

1. If a 3 foot stake casts a shadow 7 feet long, then the height of a tree, in feet, which casts a shadow 63 feet long is

   (A) 18   (B) 21   (C) 24.5   (D) 27   (E) 30.5

1969-J-18

2. A water skier being towed up an inclined ramp AB,
    as shown, is two feet above water when he is at a
    point ten feet from the upper end. If the upper end
    of the ramp is eight feet above water, the length of
    the ramp, in feet, is

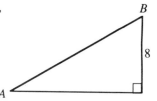

    (A) 13   (B) 30   (C) 40

    (D) $\frac{25}{2}$ (E) $\frac{40}{3}$

1976-J-15

3. ABC is a right-angled triangle with $AB = 4$ and
    $AC = 3$. If the triangle is folded along the line
    XY, vertex C coincides with the vertex B. The
    length of XY is

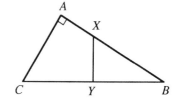

    (A) $\frac{8}{3}$ (B) $\frac{5}{3}$ (C) $\frac{15}{8}$

    (D) $\frac{10}{3}$ (E) $\frac{5}{4}$

1977-J-20

4. S and T are the midpoints of QP
    and PR, respectively. The ratio of
    the area of $SUVTP$ to the area of
    PQR is

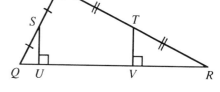

    (A) $1:2$ (B) $2:3$
    (C) $4:5$ (D) $2:5$
    (E) $3:4$

1987-F-19

5. In the adjacent squares shown, the vertices A, B,
    and C lie in a straight line. The value of x is

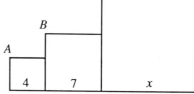

    (A) 10   (B) $\frac{49}{4}$ (C) 11

    (D) $\frac{33}{4}$ (E) $\frac{77}{4}$

1973-J-25

6. *PBCQ* is a trapezoid in which $PQ : BC = 2 : 3$. If the area of triangle *ABC* is 36, then the area of *PBCQ* is

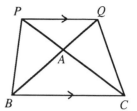

   (A) 72   (B) 84   (C) 90

   (D) 100   (E) 120

1965-J-26

7. The area of a triangle is trisected by line segments parallel to one side. If the length of that side is 12, then the length of the longer of the line segments is

   (A) 8   (B) $4\sqrt{6}$ (C) $4\sqrt{3}$ (D) $6\sqrt{2}$ (E) 6

1983-F-24

8. In the diagram, *AB* is parallel to *DC*, $AD > BC$, and $DC : AB = k$, where $k > 1$. The ratio $(AD^2 - BC^2) : (DB^2 - AC^2)$ equals

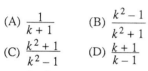

   (A) $\dfrac{1}{k + 1}$ (B) $\dfrac{k^2 - 1}{k^2 + 1}$

   (C) $\dfrac{k^2 + 1}{k^2 - 1}$ (D) $\dfrac{k + 1}{k - 1}$

   (E) $\dfrac{k - 1}{k + 1}$

1969-J-20

9. In the diagram, *F* and *E* trisect *AC*, and *G* and *H* bisect *BC* and *BF*, respectively. Then

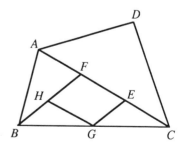

   (A) $BH = CE$ (B) $HG = GE$

   (C) $GF = \dfrac{1}{2}AB$ (D) $HG \perp GE$

   (E) *HGEF* is a parallelogram

1974-J-23

10. In the diagram, $BE = 4$ and $EC = 2$. Then the ratio of the area of parallelogram $DECF$ to the area of triangle ADF is

    (A) 4 : 1   (B) 2 : 1   (C) 5 : 1
    (D) 3 : 1   (E) 1 : 1

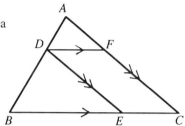

1972-J-27

11. In parallelogram $ABCD$, $AE : ED = 1 : 2$. The ratio of the area of triangle ABF to the area of quadrilateral $EFCD$ is

    (A) 1 : 4   (B) 1 : 3   (C) 2 : 5
    (D) 3 : 11   (E) none of these

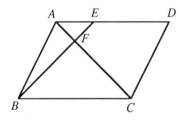

1970-J-25

12. A square has a diagonal drawn, and then is successively subdivided by lines perpendicular to preceding lines, as shown. If A, B, C, D, and E are the feet of successive perpendiculars, the ratio of the shaded area to the area of the original square is

    (A) 1 : 64   (B) 1 : 32$\sqrt{2}$ (C) 1 : 128
    (D) 1 : 64$\sqrt{2}$ (E) none of these

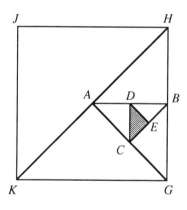

1968-J-23

13. In the diagram $AX = YB = \frac{1}{2}XY$. Z divides AC internally in the ratio 2 : 3. The ratio of the area of triangle YBC to the area of triangle ZYC is

    (A) 5 : 12   (B) 5 : 9   (C) 2 : 9
    (D) 10 : 9   (E) 2 : 3

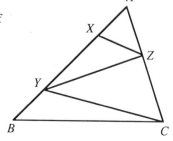

1988-F-23

14. In triangle *ABC*, medians *AE* and *BD* intersect at *F*. If $\angle BAC = \angle AFB = 90°$, and *AB* = 12, then the length of *BC* is

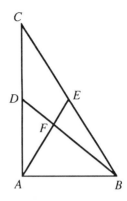

(A) 13   (B) 18   (C) 24

(D) $12\sqrt{2}$ (E) $12\sqrt{3}$

Full Solution Questions

1977-J-13

1. The legs of a right-angled triangle are 5 and 10 while the hypotenuse of a similar triangle is 15. What is the area of the larger triangle?

1972-J-17

2. The sides of a triangle are 10, 24, and 26. Find the perpendicular distance from the midpoint of the shortest side to the longest side.

1981-J-20

3. In the diagram, *AD* = *DB* = 5, *EC* = 2*AE* = 8, and angle *AED* = 90°. Find the length of *BC*.

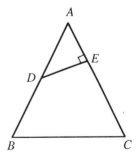

1979-J-21

4. *ABC* is a right-angled triangle with *AB* = 2*BC*. Find the ratio of the area of the inscribed square *DEFB* to the area of the triangle *ABC*.

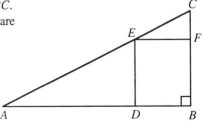

1969-J-29

5. A staircase was constructed as in the diagram. If
    $AB = BC = CD = 4$ units and $DE = 1$ unit, what
    is the length of BN?

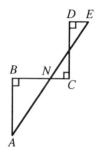

1985-F-23

6. The medians of triangle ABC are AD, BE, and CF. X, Y, and Z are taken so
    that AX, BY, and CZ are $\frac{3}{5}$ of AD, BE, and CF respectively. Determine the ratio
    of the area of triangle XYZ to the area of triangle ABC.

1970-J-28

7. In the diagram, $BD = 2$, $BC = 8$, and the angles
    marked are equal. Find AB.

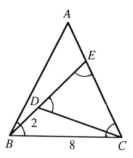

1980-J-27

8. ABC is a triangle with $AB = 3$, $BC = 4$, and $AC = 5$. The bisector of $\angle A$ meets
    BC at D. The right bisector of AD meets AB at X and AC at Y. Find the length
    of XY.

1964-J-28

9. ABCD is a parallelogram. A straight line intersects
    diagonal AC at E, side AD at F, and side CD
    extended at G. If BE and EF are 24 and 18
    respectively, find FG.

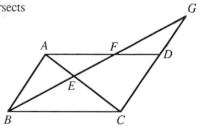

1989-C-21

10. In $\triangle ABC$, D divides AB in the ratio $1:2$, and E divides BC in the ratio $3:4$. If the area of $\triangle BDE$ is 6, find the area of $\triangle ABC$.

1975-J-19

11. Determine the value of y in the diagram.

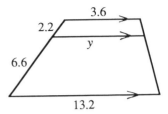

1986-F-23

12. $ABCD$ is a square in which $AE:EB = CF:FD = 2:1$. Find the ratio of the area of the parallelogram $EGFH$ to the area of the square $ABCD$.

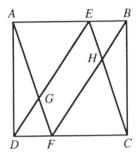

1973-J-27

13. In the diagram, $DE:EC = 2:1$ and $AB = DC = 30$. Determine the length of FG.

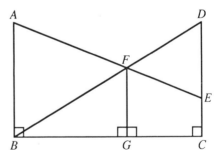

1971-J-30

14. In triangle ABC, D is the point dividing BC in the ratio $5:3$ and E is the point dividing AD in the ratio $5:3$. BE is extended to meet AC at F. Determine the ratio $AF:FC$.

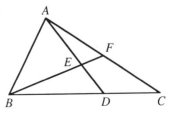

A rectangular sheet of paper ABCD is 3 inches in width and 4 inches in length. If the paper is folded so that the two diagonally opposite corners A and C coincide, how long, in inches, is the crease?

Challenge Problems

Multiple Choice Questions

1972-J-25

1. A cask is filled with 45 gallons of wine. Nine gallons are removed, and the cask is refilled with water. Then nine gallons of the mixture are removed and the cask is refilled with water again. The ratio of water to wine in the final mixture is

(A) 6 : 25   (B) 9 : 16   (C) 2 : 3   (D) 2 : 5   (E) none of these

1967-J-27

2. In the diagram $PQ = 8$, $TS = 12$, $QS = 20$, and $QR = x$. If PRT is a right angle, then

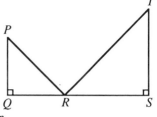

(A) x has two possible values whose difference is 4
(B) x has two possible values whose sum is 28
(C) x has only one value and $x \geq 10$
(D) x has only one value and $x < 10$
(E) x cannot be determined from the given information

1971-J-29

3. The distance between the centres of two circles is k. Their radii are respectively m and n, $(m > n)$. These circles will intersect in two distinct points if and only if

(A) $m - n < 2k < m + n$ (B) $2(m - n) < k < 2(m + n)$
(C) $2m - n < k < 2m + n$ (D) $m - n < k^2 < m + n$
(E) $m - n < k < m + n$

1975-J-27

4. If $x^2 + 4x + 6$ is a factor of $x^4 + rx^2 + s$, then $r + s$ is

(A) 10   (B) 32   (C) 20   (D) 52   (E) none of these

1973-J-30

5. If f is a function such that for all integers m and n, $f(m, 1) = m$ and $f(m, n) = f(m + 1, n - 1)$, then $f(2137, 842)$ equals

(A) 2977   (B) 2978   (C) 2979   (D) 2980   (E) 5955

1979-J-29

6. If a, b, and c are real numbers such that $a^2 + b^2 + c^2 = 1$, then the minimum value of $ab + bc + ca$ is

(A) -1 (B) $-\frac{1}{3}$ (C) 0 (D) $\frac{1}{2}$ (E) $-\frac{1}{2}$

1967-J-28

7. If $a^x = c^q = b$ and $c^y = a^z = d$, then

(A) $xy = qz$ (B) $\frac{x}{y} = \frac{q}{z}$ (C) $x^y = q^z$ (D) $x - y = q - z$ (E) $x + y = q + z$

1974-J-27

8. If $3x^2 + Kxy - 2y^2 - 7x + 7y - 6$ is the product of two linear factors with integral coefficients, then K equals

(A) -1 (B) 1 (C) -5 (D) 5 (E) 7

1968-J-28

9. Three spherical ball bearings, each of radius one inch, are resting on a smooth table, and held in contact with each other by a hollow cylinder of height two inches. The internal radius of this cylinder, in inches, is

(A) $\dfrac{\sqrt{3} + 2}{2}$ (B) $\sqrt{3} + 1$ (C) $\dfrac{\sqrt{3} + 3}{3}$ (D) $\dfrac{\sqrt{3} + 6}{3}$ (E) $\dfrac{2\sqrt{3} + 3}{3}$

1965-J-27

10. If x is a real number, the inequality $\dfrac{3}{2 - x} \le 1$ is equivalent to

(A) $x \le -1$ (B) $x \ge -1, x \ne 2$ (C) $x \le -1$ or $x \ge 0, x \ne 2$
(D) $x \le -1$ or $x > 2$ (E) $x \le -1$ or $x \ge -1, x \ne 2$

1981-J-21

11. If $z^x = y^{2x}$, $2^z = 2(4^x)$, and $x + y + z = 16$, then a possible value for y is

(A) $-\dfrac{3}{11}$ (B) $\dfrac{11}{3}$ (C) -3 (D) $\dfrac{3}{11}$ (E) none of these

1978-J-23

12. Fifteen lines drawn in a plane, with no three concurrent and no two parallel, divide the plane into 121 non-overlapping regions. Some of these regions are completely bounded by line segments and some are not. The number which are completely bounded by line segments is

(A) 45 (B) 81 (C) 30 (D) 75 (E) 91

1972-J-30

13. If $f(x - y) = f(x)f(y)$ for all x and y, and $f(x)$ never equals 0, then $f(3)$ is equal to

(A) -3 (B) 3 (C) 9 (D) ± 1 (E) none of these

Full Solution Questions

1969-J-24

1. Three ex-teenagers find that the product of their ages is 17710. Determine their ages.

1964-J-29

2. Our number system has base 10 and uses the digits 0 to 9 inclusive. A number system with base 8 uses the 8 digits 0 to 7 inclusive. If 267 and 135 are numbers in the system using base 8, find their sum.

1976-J-25

3. If $7^y - 7^{y-2} = 336\sqrt{7}$, solve for y.

1963-J-28

4. When riding on a train a person often listens to the click of the rails as the wheels pass over their joints. If the rails are each 30 feet long, for how many seconds must a person count clicks in order that the number of clicks counted will exactly equal the measure of the speed of the train in miles per hour?

1977-J-24

5. In the diagram, AB is tangent to the unshaded circles and has length 10. If the centres of the circles lie on CD, find the area of the shaded region.

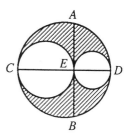

1966-J-31

6. Determine the number of positive integral solutions of the equation
$$a^2 - 7a + b^2 - 7b + 2ab = 0.$$

1981-J-29

7. The regular octagon shown is inscribed in a circle whose radius is 1 and P is any point on the circle. Find the numerical value of
$$PA^2 + PB^2 + \ldots + PH^2.$$

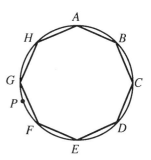

1972-J-29

8. If $x^2 + 3xy + y^2 = 60$, where x and y are real, determine the maximum possible value of xy.

1973-J-29

9. Determine the number of integral solutions of $|x| \cdot |y| \cdot |z| = 12$.

1969-J-32

10. 105 quarters are lying on a flat surface with their edges in contact. They are just contained by a frame in the form of an equilateral triangle. If the inside perimeter of the frame is 42 inches, find the radius of a quarter.

1968-J-27

11. *DEFGKM* is a regular hexagon. If P, Q, and R are the midpoints of *EF*, *GK*, and *DM*, respectively, find the ratio of the perimeter of triangle *PQR* to the perimeter of hexagon *DEFGKM*.

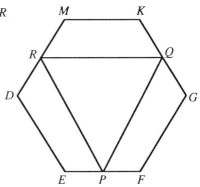

1966-J-32

12. A rectangular sheet of paper *ABCD* is three inches in width and four inches in length. The paper is folded so that the two diagonally opposite corners *A* and *C* coincide. Determine the length of the crease in the paper.

1965-J-32

13. If x, y, and z are unequal real numbers whose sum is zero and whose product is two, determine the value of $x^3 + y^3 + z^3$.

1964-J-32

14. Among grandfather's papers an old bill was found: "72 Turkeys $\$\_67.9\_$." The first and last digits of the number that represented the total price of the turkeys are replaced here with blanks as they had faded and are now illegible. What are the missing digits?

1980-J-29

15. Let f be a real-valued function such that $f(m + n) = f(m)f(n)$. If $f(4) = 256$ and $f(k) = 0.0625$, find the value of k.

Solutions

Percentages

Multiple Choice Questions

1. 1000% of $2 = \frac{1000}{100}(2) = 20$.
    The answer is D.

2. 115% of $15 = 1.15 \times 15 = 17.25$.
    The nearest whole number is 17.
    The answer is C.

3. Solution 1
    $\frac{1}{10}$ of $1\% = \frac{1}{10} \times \frac{1}{100} = \frac{1}{1000} = 0.001$.

    Solution 2
    $\frac{1}{10}$ of $1\% = 0.1 \times 0.01 = 0.001$.
    The answer is D.

4. 0.75% of $264 = \frac{0.75}{100} \times 264$
    $= 0.0075 \times 264$
    $= 1.98$.
    The answer is D.

5. The number of students wearing glasses is 40% of $30 = 0.4 \times 30 = 12$.
    Of these, $\frac{3}{12}$ or 25% are left-handed.
    The answer is B.

6. The failure rate, in percent, is $\frac{3}{16} \times 100 = 18\frac{3}{4}$.
    The answer is A.

7. The interest on the loan was $\$4200 - \$3500 = \$700$.
    The annual rate of interest was $\frac{700}{3500} \times 100\% = 20\%$.
    The answer is C.

8. Solution 1
    If 2% of the number is 8, then 1% of the number is 4, and 100% of the number is 400.

Solution 2

Let the number be x.

Then $\frac{2}{100}x = 8$.

Hence $x = \frac{100}{2}(8) = 400$.

The answer is D.

9. Let the original cost of the article be x.

The price is reduced $\frac{20}{100}x = \frac{1}{5}x$.

Hence, the reduced price is $x - \frac{1}{5}x = \frac{4}{5}x$.

Since $\frac{125}{100}\left(\frac{4}{5}x\right) = x$, the reduced price must be increased by 25% to restore the original price.

The answer is C.

10. If the cost of the T-shirt before tax is x dollars then

$$107\% \text{ of } x = 3.73$$
$$1.07x = 3.73$$
$$x = \frac{3.73}{1.07}$$
$$= 3.49.$$

The price of the shirt before tax, to the nearest cent, is $3.49.

The answer is C.

11. Solution 1

After the 25% discount, the price of the skis was $0.75 \times 90 = \$67.50$.

After a further 10% discount, the price of the skis was $0.90 \times 67.50 = \$60.75$.

Solution 2

The final price of the skis was $0.75 \times 0.90 \times 90 = \$60.75$.

The answer is E.

12. Since the team plays $20 + 25 + 15 = 60$ games, it must win
60% of $60 = 0.6 \times 60 = 36$ games.

Since the team has only 15 games remaining and requires 16 wins, it is impossible for the team to qualify for the playoffs.

The answer is E.

13. Since multiplication is associative, it does not matter in which order the discounts are applied.

i.e. $(0.80)(0.90)(0.95)10 = (0.80)(0.95)(0.90)10$
$$= (0.95)(0.80)(0.90)10$$
$$= (0.90)(0.80)(0.95)10$$
$$= 6.84.$$

The answer is E.

14. <u>Solution 1</u>
    Let the initial cost of living be x.
    After one year it is $\frac{110}{100} x = 1.1x$.
    After two years it is $\frac{110}{100} (1.1x) = 1.21x$.
    After three years it is $\frac{110}{100} (1.21x) = 1.331x$.
    The increase is $1.331x - x = 0.331x$.
    This represents an increase of 33.1%.

    <u>Solution 2</u>
    If the initial cost of living is 100%, after three years the cost is
    $(1.1)(1.1)(1.1) = 133.1\%$.
    This represents an increase of 33.1%.
    The answer is C.

15. Let the costs of the two pipes be x and y.
    Then $\frac{120}{100} x = 1.20$ and $\frac{80}{100} y = 1.20$.
    Hence $x = 1.00$ and $y = 1.50$.
    Since the total cost was \$2.50 and the total sale price was \$2.40, he lost 10 cents.
    The answer is D.

16. Let the original length of the patio be a and the
    original width be b.
    The length and width of the enlarged patio are $1.1a$
    and $1.1b$, respectively.
    The original area is ab and the new area is
    $(1.1a)(1.1b) = 1.21ab$.
    The increase in area is $1.21ab - ab = 0.21ab$
    which is a 21% increase.
    The answer is C.

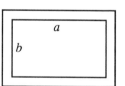

17. Let the side of the original cube be x. Then its volume is x^3.
    The side of the enlarged cube is $2x$ so its volume is $(2x)^3 = 8x^3$.
    The increase in volume is $\left(\frac{8x^3 - x^3}{x^3} \right) \times 100\% = 700\%$.
    The answer is B.

18. If the original number is x, the result obtained by dividing by 5 is $\frac{1}{5}x$.
    The correct result is $5x$.

The percentage error is $\left(\dfrac{5\ddot{x}-\frac{1}{5}x}{5x}\right)100 = \left(\dfrac{\frac{24}{5}x}{5x}\right)100$

$$= \left(\dfrac{24}{25}\right)100$$

$$= 96.$$

The answer is D.

Full Solution Questions

1. <u>Solution 1</u>

    $\frac{1}{2}\%$ of $900 = \dfrac{1}{200}(900)$

    $$= \dfrac{9}{2}$$

    $$= 4\dfrac{1}{2}\ .$$

    <u>Solution 2</u>

    1% of 900 = 9.

    Therefore, $\frac{1}{2}\%$ of $900 = \dfrac{9}{2}$

    $$= 4\dfrac{1}{2}\ .$$

2. <u>Solution 1</u>

    $\frac{2}{3}\%$ of $600 = \dfrac{2}{300} \times 600 = 4.$

    <u>Solution 2</u>

    1% of 600 = 6.

    Therefore, $\frac{2}{3}\%$ of $600 = \frac{2}{3}(6) = 4$.

3. Since 200% of 20 is 40, then 20 increased by 200% of itself is 20 + 40 = 60.

4. The price after successive reductions of 20% and 10% was
    (0.8)(0.9)(55) = \$39.60.
    The total reduction was \$55.00 − \$39.60 = \$15.40.

5. Since Janet shot down 12 invaders with 50 shots, $\dfrac{12}{50} \times 100\% = 24\%$ of her shots
    were hits.

6. The annual rate of interest is $\dfrac{180}{1200} \times 100\% = 15\%$.

7. $\dfrac{10}{100}x = \dfrac{25}{100}(16)$

   $x = \dfrac{25 \times 16}{10}$

   $= 40.$

8. If the capacity of the hall is x people, then

   $\dfrac{90}{100}x = 4131$

   $x = \dfrac{41310}{9}$

   $= 4590.$

   Thus, the capacity of the hall is 4590 people.

9. If the number of tickets sold was x, then

   $\dfrac{0.08}{100}x = 2$

   $x = \dfrac{200}{0.08}$

   $= 2500.$

   Therefore, 2500 tickets were sold.

10. The team plays a total of $75 + 45 = 120$ games.

    For a 60% winning percentage, it must win a total of $0.6 \times 120 = 72$ games.

    Since the team has already won 50 games, it must win 22 of its remaining 45 games.

11. The reduced price for the drill is $\dfrac{90}{100}(14) = \$12.60.$

    The sales tax is $\dfrac{7}{100} \times \$12.60 = \$.88.$

    Joe would pay a total price of $\$12.60 + \$.88 = \$13.48.$

12. Let x represent the price, in cents, of the wax before tax is added.

    Then, $1.05x = 120$

    $x = \dfrac{120}{1.05}.$

    The new price is 70% of $x = 0.70\left(\dfrac{120}{1.05}\right) = 80$ cents.

13. Since one Big McBurger weighs $\dfrac{1}{4} \times 16 = 4$ ounces, the water content is

    $\dfrac{20}{100} \times 4 = 0.8$ ounces.

14. The value of the 30 American dollars is $1.30 \times 30 = 39$ Canadian dollars.

    Then the tourist's change, in Canadian dollars, should be $39 - 35 = \$4.00.$

15. Harry's increased salary is

$$100\% \text{ of } 360 = \frac{110}{100} \times 360$$
$$= \$396.00.$$

His reduced work week is

$$90\% \text{ of } 44 = \frac{90}{100} \times 44$$
$$= 39.6 \text{ hours.}$$

Therefore, his new hourly rate is $\frac{396}{39.6} = \$10$ per hour.

16. Let the original length and width be l and w respectively. The new dimensions are $1.15l$ and $0.8w$.

The new area is $(1.15l)(0.8w) = 0.92lw$.

Thus, the new area is 8% less than the original area.

17. If Sue had x wrong answers, she had $1.5x$ right answers.

Since $x + 1.5x = 30$,

$$x = \frac{30}{2.5}$$
$$= 12.$$

Therefore, Sue had 18 answers correct.

18. Solution 1

Let Miss Benson's income be x. Then Mr. Afton's income is $\frac{5}{8}x$.

Since Mr. Afton saves 40% of his income, his expenses are $\frac{60}{100}\left(\frac{5}{8}x\right) = \frac{3}{8}x$.

Therefore, Miss Benson's expenses are $2\left(\frac{3}{8}x\right) = \frac{3}{4}x$.

Hence, Miss Benson saves $\frac{1}{4}x$ or 25% of her income.

Solution 2

Let Miss Benson's income be $8x$ and let her expenses be $2y$.

Then Mr. Afton's income is $5x$ and his expenses are y.

Since Mr. Afton saves 40% of his income,

$$5x - y = 0.4(5x)$$
$$y = 3x.$$

Miss Benson saves $\frac{8x - 2y}{8x} = \frac{2x}{8x} = \frac{1}{4}$ or 25% of her income.

Linear Equations

Multiple Choice Questions

1. $15x + 20 = 25$
    $$15x = 5$$
    $$x = \frac{1}{3} .$$
    The answer is C.

2. <u>Solution 1</u>
    $0.02y = 1$
    $$y = \frac{1}{0.02}$$
    $$= \frac{100}{2}$$
    $$= 50.$$

    <u>Solution 2</u>
    $0.02y = 1$
    Multiply by 50: $y = 50$
    The answer is E.

3. $\frac{2}{3}x = 0.6$
    Multiply both sides of the equation by $\frac{3}{2}$.
    $$x = \frac{3}{2}(0.6)$$
    $$= 0.9$$
    The answer is B.

4. $\frac{4}{5}x = 9.$
    To obtain $2x$ on the left side, multiply both sides of the equation by $\frac{5}{2}$.
    $$\left(\frac{5}{2}\right)\left(\frac{4}{5}\right)x = \left(\frac{5}{2}\right)(9)$$
    $$2x = 22.5$$
    The answer is B.

5. $5x - 3 = ax$
    $$5x - ax = 3$$
    $$x(5 - a) = 3$$
    $$x = \frac{3}{5-a}, \text{ since } a \neq 5.$$
    The answer is E.

6. Since $x = 2k$, $k = \frac{x}{2}$.

    Therefore $\frac{1}{k} = \frac{2}{x}$.

    Hence $y = \frac{4}{k} = \frac{8}{x}$.

    The answer is B.

7. $\begin{aligned} a + 2b - 8c &= 2b + 2b - 8c \\ &= 4b - 8c \\ &= 16c - 8c \\ &= 8c. \end{aligned}$

    The answer is B.

8. Solution 1

    Since $x = 7$ and $xy = 91$, $y = 13$.

    Therefore $x + 2y = 7 + 26 = 33$.

    Solution 2

    $\begin{aligned} x + 2y &= x + \frac{2xy}{x} \\ &= 7 + \frac{182}{7} \\ &= 33. \end{aligned}$

    The answer is C.

9. Solution 1

    Since one-half of the number is $39 - 15 = 24$, then the original number is 48.

    Solution 2

    Let the original number be x.

    $\begin{aligned} \tfrac{1}{2}x + 15 &= 39 \\ x + 30 &= 78 \\ x &= 48. \end{aligned}$

    The answer is C.

10. Since $\frac{1}{x} = \frac{5}{a}$, $x = \frac{a}{5}$.

    Therefore $\frac{a}{5} = \frac{c}{6}$, so $\frac{c}{a} = \frac{6}{5}$.

    The answer is E.

11. Since all the angles in the diagram sum to 360°,

$$3x + 90 = 360$$
$$3x = 270$$
$$x = 90.$$

The answer is C.

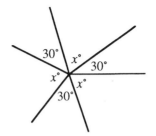

12. $$3x + 7 = 7x + 15$$
$$-4x = 8$$
$$x = -2 .$$

Since $x^2 + k = 7x + 15$
$$4 + k = -14 + 15$$
$$k = -3.$$

The answer is B.

13. $$s = p + \frac{1}{2}rp^2$$
$$\frac{1}{2}rp^2 = s - p$$
$$rp^2 = 2s - 2p$$
$$r = \frac{2s - 2p}{p^2}$$

The answer is A.

14. Let the cost of the pencil be x cents.
Then the cost of the pen is $(x + 100)$ cents.

$$x + (x + 100) = 140$$
$$2x = 40$$
$$x = 20.$$

Therefore the pencil costs 20 cents.
The answer is E.

15. Since the perimeter of the figure is 58,

$$2(y + 7) + 2y + 2(y + 4) + (y + 1) = 58$$
$$7y + 23 = 58$$
$$7y = 35$$
$$y = 5.$$

The answer is B.

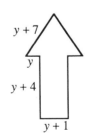

16. Since the reciprocal of $\frac{3x}{4}$ is $\frac{1}{12}$, then $\frac{3x}{4} = 12$

$$3x = 48$$

$$x = 16.$$

The answer is D.

17. $(x, 3) \blacklozenge (-2, 5) = 3$

$$-2x + 15 = 3$$

$$-2x = -12$$

$$x = 6.$$

The answer is E.

18.
$$y = \frac{x - 2}{x + 1}$$

$$xy + y = x - 2$$

$$xy - x = -y - 2$$

$$x(y - 1) = -y - 2$$

$$x = \frac{-y - 2}{y - 1}$$

$$= \frac{y + 2}{1 - y}.$$

The answer is E.

19. Since 200 ml is 0.8 or $\frac{4}{5}$ of the capacity of the glass, then it requires $\frac{5}{4} \times 200 = 250$ ml of liquid to fill the glass.

The answer is E.

20.
$$\frac{a}{x - b} = \frac{b}{x - a}$$

$$ax - a^2 = bx - b^2$$

$$ax - bx = a^2 - b^2$$

$$(a - b)x = (a - b)(a + b)$$

Since $a \neq b$, $x = a + b$.

The answer is C.

21. Let the weight of a brick be x pounds.

$$x + \frac{5}{16} = \frac{12}{16} + \frac{3}{4}x$$

$$\frac{1}{4}x = \frac{7}{16}$$

$$x = \frac{7}{4}.$$

Therefore a brick weight $\frac{7}{4}$ pounds.

The answer is B.

22. <u>Solution 1</u>

Since 2 gallons increases the amount from $\frac{1}{6}$ to $\frac{1}{4}$ of a tank, then 2 gallons is

$\frac{1}{4} - \frac{1}{6} = \frac{1}{12}$ of a tank.

Hence the capacity of the tank is $2 \times 12 = 24$ gallons.

<u>Solution 2</u>

Let the capacity of the tank be x gallons.

$$\text{Then, } \tfrac{1}{6}x + 2 = \tfrac{1}{4}x$$
$$\tfrac{1}{4}x - \tfrac{1}{6}x = 2$$
$$\tfrac{1}{12}x = 2$$
$$x = 24.$$

The capacity of the tank is 24 gallons.

The answer is D.

23. Let the angles of the triangle be A, B, and C with $A < B < C$.

Then $C = A + 35$ and $B = A + 10$.

But $A + B + C = 180$.

$$\text{Therefore } A + (A + 10) + (A + 35) = 180$$
$$3A + 45 = 180$$
$$3A = 135$$
$$A = 45.$$

The answer is B.

24. Since $1^3 = 1$, then $-1 - x = 1$ and $x = -2$.

The answer is E.

Full Solution Questions

1. $2x + 5 = 9x - 13$
   $-7x = -18$
   $x = \dfrac{18}{7}.$

2. $0.4x = \dfrac{2}{3}$

   $\dfrac{4}{10}x = \dfrac{2}{3}$

   Multiply by $\dfrac{10}{4}$:

   $x = \left(\dfrac{10}{4}\right)\left(\dfrac{2}{3}\right) = \dfrac{5}{3}.$

3. $ax + c = bx$

      $ax - bx = -c$

     $x(a - b) = -c$

        $x = \dfrac{-c}{a - b}$.

4.   If $x = -2$, $x^3 - 4x^2 - kx - 20 = 0$

                $-8 - 16 + 2k - 20 = 0$

                      $2k = 44$

                      $k = 22$.

5.   Substitute $a = 12$ and $c = 12$ in $a = 30 - bc$ to give

      $12 = 30 - 12b$

    $12b = 18$

      $b = \dfrac{3}{2}$.

   If $a = 21$, we get

     $21 = 30 - \dfrac{3}{2} c$

   $\dfrac{3}{2} c = 9$

     $c = 6$.

6. $\dfrac{1}{3} + \dfrac{1}{4} + \dfrac{1}{n} = 1$

         $\dfrac{1}{n} = 1 - \dfrac{1}{3} - \dfrac{1}{4}$

         $\dfrac{1}{n} = \dfrac{5}{12}$

         $n = \dfrac{12}{5}$.

7. $y = \dfrac{2x - 3}{x + 6}$

   If $y = -2$, $\dfrac{2x - 3}{x + 6} = -2$

            $2x - 3 = -2x - 12$

               $4x = -9$

                 $x = -\dfrac{9}{4}$.

8. If $\frac{p}{q} = -1, p = -q$.

    Hence, $p + q = 0$.

9. Since $x : y = 3 : 2$, let $x = 3k$ and $y = 2k$.

    Then $3k + 6k = 27$

    $\qquad\quad 9k = 27$

    $\qquad\quad\;\; k = 3$.

    Therefore $x = 9$ and $y = 6$.

10. Solution 1

    $ab = 16$

    $\frac{b}{c} = \frac{1}{3}$

    $\frac{c}{a} = 12$.

    Multiply the three equations:

    $(ab)\left(\frac{b}{c}\right)\left(\frac{c}{a}\right) = 16\left(\frac{1}{3}\right)(12)$

    $\qquad\quad b^2 = 64$

    $\qquad\quad\; b = \pm 8$

    Solution 2

    Since $a = \frac{16}{b}$ and $c = 3b$, then $\frac{c}{a} = \frac{3b}{\frac{16}{b}} = \frac{3b^2}{16}$.

    Therefore, $\frac{3b^2}{16} = 12$

    $\qquad\quad b^2 = 64$

    $\qquad\quad\; b = \pm 8$.

11. Since $a = b + 3$ and $c = b - 3$,

    $a^2 - 2b^2 + c^2 = (b + 3)^2 - 2b^2 + (b - 3)^2$

    $\qquad\qquad\qquad = b^2 + 6b + 9 - 2b^2 + b^2 - 6b + 9$

    $\qquad\qquad\qquad = 18$.

12. If $\frac{5}{6}$ of a number is 60, the number is $\frac{6}{5} \times 60 = 72$.

    Therefore $\frac{3}{4}$ of the original number is $\frac{3}{4} \times 72 = 54$.

13. Let x represent the number of tapes that Mary has.

Tim and Sue have $(x - 5)$ and $(x - 12)$ tapes, respectively.

$$x + (x - 5) + (x - 12) = 73$$
$$3x = 90$$
$$x = 30.$$

Mary has 30 tapes.

14. If the reciprocal of $\frac{1}{x} - 1$ is -2,

then $\frac{1}{x} - 1 = -\frac{1}{2}$
$$\frac{1}{x} = \frac{1}{2}$$
$$x = 2.$$

15. Let x represent the number of each kind of stamp.

Then $35x + 30x = 2275$
$$65x = 2275$$
$$x = 35.$$

A total of $2 \times 35 = 70$ stamps were purchased.

16. Solution 1

Let x be the number of oranges he must sell. Since he sells them at 9 cents each and buys them at $\frac{25}{3}$ cents each, then $9x - \frac{25}{3}x = 300$
$$27x - 25x = 900$$
$$2x = 900$$
$$x = 450.$$
He must sell 450 oranges to make a profit of \$3.00.

Solution 2

Since the grocer's cost per orange is $\frac{25}{3}$ cents and his selling price is 9 cents per orange, his profit is $9 - \frac{25}{3} = \frac{2}{3}$ cents per orange.

To make a profit of \$3.00 he must sell $300 \div \frac{2}{3} = 450$ oranges.

17. Let the total amount of prize money be x dollars.

She won $\frac{7}{10}x$ and, after spending $\frac{3}{4}$ of her winnings, she was left with

$\frac{1}{4}\left(\frac{7}{10}x\right) = \frac{7}{40}x.$

Therefore, $\frac{7}{40}x = 2100$

$$7x = 84\ 000$$

$$x = 12\ 000.$$

The total amount of prize money available in the lottery was \$12 000.

18. $2x + (x + 40) + x = 180$

$$4x = 140$$

$$x = 35.$$

The largest angle is $35 + 40 = 75$ degrees.

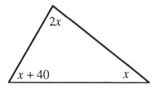

19. $(2x - 5) - (-3x + 4) = 2$

$$5x = 11$$

$$x = \frac{11}{5}.$$

20. Let the length of the shortest piece be x m.

Then the other pieces have lengths $3x$ m and $12x$ m.

$$x + 3x + 12x = 64$$

$$16x = 64$$

$$x = 4.$$

The shortest piece is 4 m long.

21. Let the length of PR be x. Then the lengths of PQ and QR are each $3x$.

(Note that it is impossible to form an isosceles triangle with sides of lengths x, x, and $3x$).

Since the perimeter is 35,

then $x + 3x + 3x = 35$

$$7x = 35$$

$$x = 5.$$

Hence the length of PQ is 15.

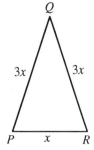

22. Since opposite sides of a parallelogram are equal,

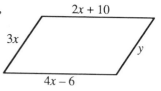

$$2x + 10 = 4x - 6$$
$$-2x = -16$$
$$x = 8.$$

    Therefore $y = 3x = 24$.

23. We are given that $\frac{1}{3} - \frac{1}{5} = \frac{1}{5} - \frac{1}{c}$.

    Therefore, $\frac{1}{c} = \frac{1}{5} + \frac{1}{5} - \frac{1}{3}$
    $$\frac{1}{c} = \frac{1}{15}$$
    $$c = 15.$$

24. Solution 1

    If N is doubled and increased by 5 we get $2N + 5$.
    If this quantity is doubled we get $2(2N + 5) = 38$
    Therefore, $4N + 10 = 38$
    $$4N = 28$$
    $$N = 7.$$

    Solution 2

    We could start at 38 and reverse the operations to find N.
    $$2N = (38 \div 2) - 5$$
    $$= 14$$
    Therefore $N = 7$.

25. Let the number be x.
    $$2x + 8 = 3x - 2$$
    $$-x = -10$$
    $$x = 10.$$
    The number is 10.

Circumferences of Circles

Multiple Choice Questions

1. The circumference of a circle is $2\pi r$.
    Hence $2\pi r = 6\pi$
    $r = 3$.
    The answer is A.

2. Since the circumference of a circle is $2\pi r$,
    $2\pi r = 40$
    $r = \dfrac{20}{\pi}$.
    Hence the radius is $\dfrac{20}{\pi}$ cm.
    The answer is C.

3. If the radius of the circle is r, the perimeter is $2\pi r$.
    Thus, $2\pi r = 3$ so $r = \dfrac{3}{2\pi}$.
    The area is $\pi r^2 = \pi \left(\dfrac{3}{2\pi}\right)^2$
    $= \dfrac{9}{4\pi}$.
    The answer is B.

4. The amount of fencing needed is obtained by
    finding the circumference of the two circles formed
    by the four semicircles. Since each circle has radius
    x m, the total is $2(2\pi x) = 4\pi x$ m.
    The answer is A.

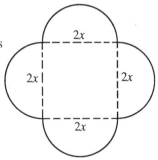

5. Let each side of the square be x and let the radius of
    the circle be r.
    Then $2\pi r = 4x$

    $$r = \frac{2x}{\pi}\,.$$

    The ratio of the area of the square to the area of the
    circle is $\dfrac{x^2}{\pi r^2} = \dfrac{x^2}{\pi\left(\dfrac{4x^2}{\pi^2}\right)}$

    $$= \frac{\pi}{4}\,.$$

    The answer is D.

6. Since $\angle PTQ = 60°$, arc PQ is one–sixth the
    circumference of the circle with centre T and
    radius 1.
    Hence arc $PQ = \frac{1}{6}(2\pi) = \frac{\pi}{3}$.
    Similarly arc $QR = $ arc $TS = \frac{\pi}{3}$.
    The perimeter of $PQRST$ is $3\left(\frac{\pi}{3}\right) + 2 = \pi + 2$.
    The answer is B.

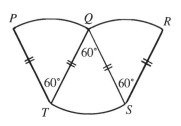

7. Since the perimeter of the square is 60, each side
    is 15. Since $3d = 15$, $d = 5$.
    The perimeter of each semicircle is $\frac{1}{2}(\pi d) = \frac{5}{2}\pi$.

    The perimeter of the figure is

    $$4\left(10 + \frac{5}{2}\pi\right) = 40 + 10\pi.$$
    The answer is A.

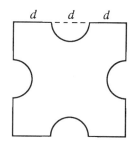

8. <u>Solution 1</u>
    The ratio of the circumference to the diameter in <u>*any*</u> circle is $\dfrac{\pi d}{d} = \dfrac{\pi}{1}$.
    <u>Solution 2</u>
    Let the radius of the original circle be r.
    Then the radius of the new circle is $r + 1$.
    The ratio of the new circumference to the new diameter is $\dfrac{2\pi(r + 1)}{2(r + 1)} = \dfrac{\pi}{1}$.

    The answer is C.

9. At each corner of the rectangle, the centre of the
    circle describes a quarter circle whose radius is r.
    The total distance travelled by the centre of the circle
    is $p + 2\pi r$.
    The answer is D.

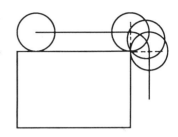

10. If the radius is r, the area is πr^2.
    If the radius is doubled, the area is $\pi(2r)^2 = 4\pi r^2$.
    Since $4\pi r^2 \neq 2(\pi r^2)$, statement (A) is incorrect.
    It is worthwhile considering each of the other four statements as well.
    In (B), if the base and altitude are b and h respectively, $\frac{1}{2}b(2h) = 2\left(\frac{1}{2}bh\right)$.
    Similarly, in (C), $(2b)h = 2(bh)$.
    In (D), if the fraction is $\left(\frac{p}{q}\right)$, $\frac{2p}{q} = 2\left(\frac{p}{q}\right)$.

    In (E), $2a < a$ if a is negative.
    Thus each of the statements (B), (C), (D), and (E) is correct.
    The answer is A.

11. There are $\dfrac{3-1}{0.02} = 100$ circles of tape on the spool.
    The middle circle of tape has radius 2 cm so its length is $2(2\pi) = 4\pi$ cm. If we
    consider the middle circle of tape to be the average length of all of them, the
    approximate length of the tape is
    $100(4\pi) = 400(3.14)$
    $\qquad\qquad = 1256$ cm or about 12.6 m.
    The answer is E.

12. Let the length of each side of the square be x
    inches. Then the length of the diagonal of the
    square is $\sqrt{x^2 + x^2} = x\sqrt{2}$.
    The circumference of the circle is $x\sqrt{2}\,\pi$ inches.
    Hence, $x\sqrt{2}\,\pi = 100$
    $$x = \frac{100}{\sqrt{2}\,\pi}$$
    $$= \frac{50\sqrt{2}}{\pi}.$$
    The answer is B.

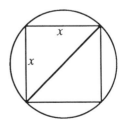

13. Each of the six curved parts of the band is one-sixth of the circumference of one of the circles.

Each of the straight parts of the band is $2(2) = 4$ units.

Hence, the length of the band is

$6\left[4 + \frac{1}{6}(4\pi)\right] = 24 + 4\pi$.

The answer is C.

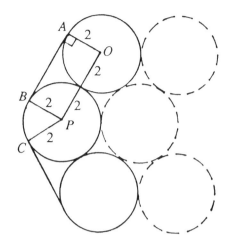

Full Solution Questions

1. The circumference is $2\pi(50) = 100\pi$ m.

2. If the radii of the larger and smaller circles are r_1 and r_2 respectively, then $r_1 - r_2 = 10$.
    The difference between their circumferences is
    $$2\pi r_1 - 2\pi r_2 = 2\pi(r_1 - r_2)$$
    $$= 2\pi(10)$$
    $$= 20\pi.$$

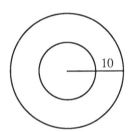

3. Let the radius of the circle be r.
    Then $2\pi r = \pi$
    $$r = \frac{1}{2} .$$
    The area is $\pi\left(\frac{1}{2}\right)^2 = \frac{\pi}{4}$.

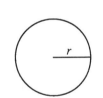

4. The length of the rectangle is 5π, the same as the circumference of the top of the can.
    Hence, the perimeter of the rectangle is $2(12 + 5\pi) = (24 + 10\pi)$ cm.

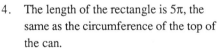

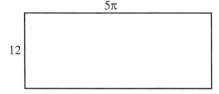

5. Let the radius of the circle be r.
    Then $\pi r^2 = 144\pi$
    $$r^2 = 144$$
    $$r = 12.$$
    The arc length is one-sixth of the circumference
    which equals $\frac{1}{6}(24\pi) = 4\pi$.

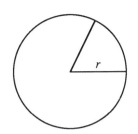

6. Let the radius of the semicircle be r inches.
    The perimeter of the sign is
    $$\frac{1}{2}(2\pi r) + 2r = 60$$
    $$\pi r + 2r = 60$$
    $$r(\pi + 2) = 60$$
    $$r = \frac{60}{\pi + 2}$$
    Hence, the radius is $\frac{60}{\pi + 2}$ inches.

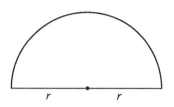

7. The length of arc $ABCD$ is $\frac{1}{2}(2\pi) = \pi$.
    Therefore, the length of arc BC is $\pi - 2$.

8. The arc length of the semicircular top is
    $\frac{1}{2}(2\pi) = \pi$ feet.
    The perimeter of the window is
    $\pi + 3 + 3 + 2 = (\pi + 8)$ feet.

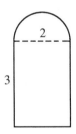

9. Let the radius of the earth be r feet. Then the radius of the belt is $(r + 1)$ feet.
    The difference in their circumferences, is $2\pi(r + 1) - 2\pi r = 2\pi$ feet.

10. Let $AB = x$. The length of the upper path
    is $\pi x + \pi x = 2\pi x$.

    The length of the lower path is
    $\pi\left(\frac{3}{2}x\right) + \pi\left(\frac{1}{2}x\right) = 2\pi x$.

    Hence, the ratio of the lengths of the two
    paths is 1:1.

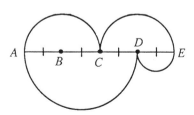

11. Solution 1

If the rods are tied as illustrated, the distance around
the figure is made up of four quarter circles plus
four tangents each of length 7 inches.
Then the length of string required is

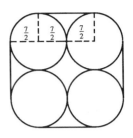

$$4\left[\frac{1}{4}(7\pi) + 7\right] + 2 = 7\pi + 30$$

$$\approx 7\left(\frac{22}{7}\right) + 30$$

$$= 52 \text{ inches.}$$

Solution 2

If the rods are tied as illustrated, the distance around
the figure is made up of two arcs each of which is $\frac{1}{3}$
of a circle, two arcs each of which is $\frac{1}{6}$ of a circle,
and four tangents each of length 7 inches.
Then the length of the string required is

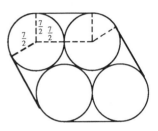

$$2\left[\frac{1}{3}(7\pi) + \frac{1}{6}(7\pi)\right] + 4(7) + 2 = 7\pi + 30$$

$$= 52 \text{ inches, as before.}$$

12. Let the circumference of the rear wheel be x feet.

The rear wheel makes a total of $\frac{5280}{x}$ revolutions in a mile.

The front wheel makes a total of $\frac{5280}{x-2}$ revolutions in a mile.

Then $\frac{5280}{x-2} - \frac{5280}{x} = 24$

Hence, $\frac{220}{x-2} - \frac{220}{x} = 1$

$$220x - 220(x-2) = x(x-2)$$

$$x^2 - 2x - 440 = 0$$

$$(x - 22)(x + 20) = 0$$

Since $x > 0$, $x = 22$.

The circumference of the rear wheel is 22 feet.

13. As a circle rolls through one revolution, its centre travels a distance equal to the circumference, and conversely. As the circle rolls from position x_1 to position x_2, its centre moves a distance equal to an arc of radius $2r$ subtending an angle of $120°$ at the centre of circle A.

The length of this arc is $\frac{120}{360} \times 4\pi r = \frac{4\pi r}{3}$.

As the circle rolls from position x_2 to position x_3 its centre travels a distance equal to an arc of radius $2r$ subtending an angle of $60°$ at the centre of circle B.

The length of this arc is $\frac{60}{360} \times 4\pi r = \frac{2\pi r}{3}$.

The total distance travelled by the centre of the rolling circle is $2\left(\frac{4\pi r}{3}\right) + 4\left(\frac{2\pi r}{3}\right) = \frac{16\pi r}{3}$.

Since each revolution is $2\pi r$, the total number of revolutions is $\frac{16\pi r}{3} \div 2\pi r = \frac{8}{3}$.

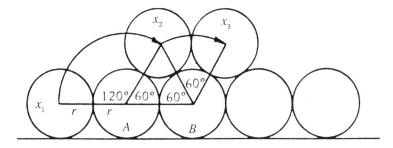

Rates

Multiple Choice Questions

1. Ann runs $\frac{1}{10}$ km in 31 seconds.

    At this same rate she would run 1 km in 310 seconds, and 8 km in 2480 seconds, which is approximately 40 minutes.

    The answer is B.

2. Running at 5 km per minute, Wonder Woman would complete 1 km in 12 seconds. Running at 3 km per minute, Superman would complete 1 km in 20 seconds. Since Wonder Woman gives Superman a 5-second head start, she would win by 3 seconds.

    The answer is A.

3. In $1\frac{1}{4}$ hours, the motorcycle travelled $\frac{5}{4} \times 60 = 75$ km.

    In $1\frac{1}{4}$ hours, the truck travelled $75 - 25 = 50$ km.

    The average speed of the truck was $50 \div 1\frac{1}{4} = 50 \times \frac{4}{5} = 40$ km/h.

    The answer is C.

4. Since the watch loses 1 second per day, it will lose 24 hours in $24 \times 60 \times 60$ days.

    This is equivalent to $\dfrac{24 \times 60 \times 60}{365}$ years which is approximately equal to

    $\dfrac{24 \times 60 \times 60}{360} = 240$ years.

    The answer is D.

5. The pump makes 26 strokes in 14 seconds.

    In one second it makes $\frac{26}{14}$ strokes.

    In one minute it makes $60 \times \frac{26}{14} = \frac{780}{7} = 111\frac{3}{7}$ strokes.

    To the nearest integer, the pumping rate is 111 strokes per minute.

    The answer is B.

6. The time elapsed for the entire trip is $\dfrac{100}{x} + \dfrac{400}{2x} + \dfrac{600}{3x} = \dfrac{100}{x} + \dfrac{200}{x} + \dfrac{200}{x}$

    $$= \dfrac{500}{x} \text{ hours.}$$

    The average speed for the entire trip is

    $\dfrac{\text{total distance}}{\text{elapsed time}} = \dfrac{1100}{\dfrac{500}{x}}$

    $$= \dfrac{11}{5}x \text{ mph.}$$

    The answer is E.

7. In r seconds, the automobile travels $\dfrac{a}{6}$ feet.

    In 1 second, it travels $\dfrac{a}{6r}$ feet.

    In 3 minutes, it travels $\dfrac{180a}{6r}$ feet.

    Since there are 3 feet in 1 yard, the distance the car travels in 3 minutes is

    $\dfrac{30a}{r} \div 3 = \dfrac{10a}{r}$ yards.

    The answer is E.

8. In one day, A could complete $\dfrac{1}{6}$ of the job and B could complete $\dfrac{1}{4}$ of the job.

    Working together, on one day, they could complete $\dfrac{1}{6} + \dfrac{1}{4} = \dfrac{2+3}{12} = \dfrac{5}{12}$ of the job.

    The number of days required to complete the entire job would be $1 \div \dfrac{5}{12} = \dfrac{12}{5}$.

    The answer is D.

9. Solution 1

    At a speed of 30 mph it takes two minutes to drive up a one-mile hill.

    To average 60 mph for a two-mile trip, the total elapsed time for the trip would be 2 minutes. Since this time has already elapsed on the uphill portion of the trip, it is impossible to average 60 mph for the whole trip.

    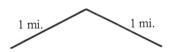

    Solution 2

    Let the speed the car must be driven on the downslope be x mph.

    The elapsed time for the uphill portion is 2 minutes.

    The time it takes to travel one mile at x mph is $\dfrac{x}{60}$ minutes.

To average 60 mph for the entire trip,

$$\frac{2}{\frac{2}{60} + \frac{x}{60}} = 60$$

$$2 = 2 + x.$$

The only value of x that would make this statement true is $x = 0$, and at that speed the car would never complete the trip. There is no possible value for x in order to average 60 mph for the whole trip.

The answer is E.

10. The distance travelled was $3 + 2 + 1 = 6$ km.

The elapsed time was $\dfrac{3}{150} + \dfrac{2}{200} + \dfrac{1}{300} = \dfrac{1}{50} + \dfrac{1}{100} + \dfrac{1}{300}$

$$= \frac{6 + 3 + 1}{300}$$

$$= \frac{1}{30} \text{ h.}$$

The average speed was $\dfrac{6}{\frac{1}{30}} = 180$ km/h.

The answer is A.

11. When Amy completed 1000 m, Brigitte had run 800 m and Cindy had run 600 m.

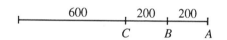

Hence, the ratio of Cindy's speed to Brigitte's speed is 6:8 or 3:4.

When Brigitte has completed 1000 m, Cindy will have completed $\dfrac{3}{4} \times 1000 = 750$ m, so Brigitte will finish 250 m ahead of Cindy.

The answer is D.

12. John walks from A to C and Sue walks from A to B to C. Since BC is in a northeast direction, $\angle ABC = \angle ACB = 45°$.

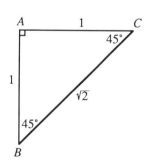

Let the distance AC that John walks equal 1 unit. Then, the distance Sue walks is $AB + BC = (1 + \sqrt{2})$ units.

Since Sue walks k times as fast as John, the distance Sue walks is k times the distance John walks.

Therefore, $k = 1 + \sqrt{2}$.

The answer is E.

13. Let the rate by boat be r km/h. Then the rate by car was $3r$ km/h.
    If the distance of the trip was d km, the distance travelled by car and boat were
    $\frac{2}{3}d$ km and $\frac{1}{3}d$ km, respectively.
    The elapsed time, in hours, for the trip was

$$\frac{\frac{2d}{3}}{3r} + \frac{\frac{d}{3}}{r} = \frac{2d}{9r} + \frac{d}{3r}$$

$$= \frac{5d}{9r}$$

$$= 3t \ .$$

The time spent in the boat was $\frac{d}{3r} = \frac{9}{5}t$ h.
The answer is C.

14. Let the point at which Moe and Joe
    meet be C, the distance AB equal 1
    (a unit distance), and the distance
    AC equal d.

If Joe's rate is r, then Moe's rate is xr.
The distance Joe and Moe walk until they meet are
d and $2 - d$, respectively.
Their walking times are equal.
Hence, $\frac{d}{r} = \frac{2-d}{xr}$

$$d = \frac{2}{1+x} \ .$$

The answer is E.

15. On the walk to Keith's house, let the distance, in km,
    on the level, uphill and downhill be a, b, c,
    respectively.

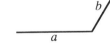

The time taken will be $\left(\frac{a}{3} + \frac{b}{2} + \frac{c}{6}\right)$ h.

For the return walk the time required is $\left(\frac{c}{2} + \frac{b}{6} + \frac{a}{3}\right)$ h.

The total time is $\frac{2a}{3} + \frac{2b}{3} + \frac{2c}{3} = 6$ h.

Hence, $a + b + c = 9$ and the total distance is 18 km.
The answer is C.

16. In the diagram, the situation at 12 noon is illustrated.
    The segment *OP*, that joins the centre of the earth to
    Pat's space capsule, rotates at the rate of 120°/h.
    The segment *OM*, that joins *O* to Mike's space
    capsule, rotates at the rate of $\frac{360}{7.5} = 48°/h$.
    In *x* hours, *OP* will rotate 120*x* degrees and *OM*
    will rotate 48*x* degrees.
    In order that *OP* and *OM* be collinear, the
    difference in the number of degees rotated must be a
    multiple of 360.
    Hence, 120*x* – 48*x* = 360*m*, *m* a positive integer
    $\qquad$ 72*x* = 360*m*.
    The next coincidence occurs when *m* = 1 and *x* = 5.
    This occurs at 5:00 p.m.
    The answer is D.

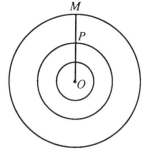

17. At normal speed, the hour hand rotates at 30°/h.
    In *x* hours, at twice its normal speed, the hour hand rotates 60*x* degrees.
    At normal speed the minute hand rotates at 360°/h.
    In *x* hours, at half its normal speed, the minute hand rotates 180*x* degrees.
    In order that the hands coincide, the difference in the number of degrees rotated must
    be a multiple of 360.
    Hence, 180*x* – 60*x* = 360*m*, *m* a positive integer
    $\qquad$ 120*x* = 360*m*.
    The next coincidence occurs when *m* = 1 and *x* = 3.
    When this occurs, both hands are pointing to the 6 and the correct time is 3:00 o'clock.
    The answer is B.

Full Solution Questions

1. At the rate of 8 km per 5 minutes, the car would travel 12 × 8 = 96 km in one hour.

2. The rate the car travels is $\frac{80}{2} = 40$ mph.
   The time it takes to drive the 290 miles
   from Hamilton to Windsor is
   $\frac{290}{40} = 7\frac{1}{4}$ hours.

3. When the last car enters the tunnel, the engine is 2000 m from the other end of the tunnel.
   The train travels 2000 m in 30 seconds so its rate is $\frac{200}{3}$ m/s.

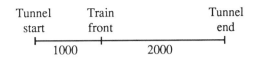

4. A runner takes x steps to run y feet.

   To run 1 foot, the runner takes $\frac{x}{y}$ steps.

   To run 1 yard, the runner takes $\frac{3x}{y}$ steps.

   To complete a hundred yard dash, the runner would take $\frac{300x}{y}$ steps.

5. The time taken to go one mile at 30 mph is $\frac{1}{30}$ h.

   The time taken to go one mile at 40 mph is $\frac{1}{40}$ h.

   The average speed for the 2 miles is $\dfrac{2}{\frac{1}{30}+\frac{1}{40}} = \frac{240}{4+3} = 34\frac{2}{7}$ mph.

6. The distance travelled in 3 laps is 360 miles.

   For the first lap, he takes $\frac{120}{60} = 2$ hours.

   For the second lap, he takes $\frac{120}{40} = 3$ hours.

   For the third lap, he takes $\frac{120}{30} = 4$ hours.

   The average speed for the three runs is $\frac{360}{9} = 40$ mph.

7. When A has completed 24 km, B and C have completed 16 km and 12 km, respectively. C runs 3 km for every 4 km B runs. To finish, B runs 8 more km. In this time, C runs 6 km and will still be 6 km from the finish line.

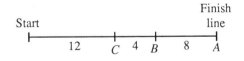

8. Let the capacity of the tub be T litres.
   The tub empties at the rate of $\frac{T}{15}$ L/min. and fills at the rate of $\frac{T}{12}$ L/min.
   If the plug is out and the tap is on, the net effect is that the tub fills at the rate of
   $\frac{T}{12} - \frac{T}{15} = \frac{T}{60}$ L/min.
   At this rate it will take 60 min. to fill the tub.

9. In one second, at 100 km/h, Nancy travels $\frac{100}{3600}$ km.

    In 10 seconds, she travels $10 \times \frac{1}{36} = \frac{5}{18}$ km.

    During this same time interval, Pat travels $\frac{1}{10} + \frac{5}{18} = \frac{34}{90}$ km.

    Since ten seconds is equivalent to $\frac{10}{3600}$ hours, the speed of Pat's car, in km/h, is

    $\frac{34}{90} \div \frac{10}{3600} = 136$.

10. Let x be the number of seconds after starting until

    they meet for the first time. The distances covered

    by the runners are $\frac{8}{3}x$ m and $\frac{7}{3}x$ m.

    Together, they have completed 110 m.

    Thus, $\frac{8}{3}x + \frac{7}{3}x = 110$

    $\qquad\qquad 15x = 330$

    $\qquad\qquad\ x = 22.$

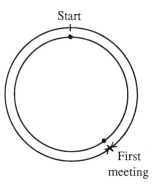

Start

First
meeting

    Continuing in this way, the runners will meet every

    22 seconds.

    In 15 minutes, the number of times they will meet is

    the greatest integer part of $\frac{15 \times 60}{22}$ which is 40.

11. Solution 1

    The trains that leave Montreal at midnight and 1:00 a.m. arrive in Toronto before 7:00
    a.m. The five trains that leave Montreal at 2:00 a.m. through 6:00 a.m. are still on the
    tracks between Montreal and Toronto. The train leaving Toronto at 7:00 a.m. will
    meet these five trains plus the six trains leaving at 7:00 a.m. through 12 noon, since it
    does not arrive in Montreal until 12:01 p.m. Thus, the number of trains it will meet is
    11.

    Solution 2

    When the train T leaves Toronto, there are 6 trains on the track (at distances 1, 61,
    121, 181, ... miles from Toronto). As T moves to Montreal (in 301 minutes), there
    is time for 5 more trains to leave Montreal. Hence, the number of trains met is
    $6 + 5 = 11$.

12. Let the distances be x and y, as shown.
    The times taken for the four legs of the
    journey were $\frac{x}{4}, \frac{y}{3}, \frac{y}{6},$ and $\frac{x}{4}$ hours,
    respectively.

    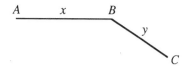

    Thus, $\frac{x}{4} + \frac{y}{3} + \frac{y}{6} + \frac{x}{4} = 6$

    $3x + 4y + 2y + 3x = 72$

    $6x + 6y = 72$

    $x + y = 12.$

    The total distance walked was $2x + 2y = 24$ miles.

13. Let the height of the candles, before lighting, be 1 unit.
    The rates of burning are $\frac{1}{4}$ candle/hour and $\frac{1}{3}$ candle/hour.
    In x hours, the heights of the two candles are $1 - \frac{x}{4}$ and $1 - \frac{x}{3}$.
    In order that the height of the first candle be double the height of the second candle,

    $1 - \frac{x}{4} = 2\left(1 - \frac{x}{3}\right)$

    $\frac{2}{3}x - \frac{x}{4} = 1$

    $8x - 3x = 12$

    $x = \frac{12}{5}$.

    In $\frac{12}{5}$ hours the height of the first candle was double that of the second candle.

14. Let the length of the bridge be $3x$, the
    distance of the train from the bridge be
    y, and the speed at which the man
    must run be s.

    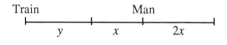

    In order that the train and man reach the
    nearer end of the bridge at the same
    time, $\frac{x}{s} = \frac{y}{45}$.   (1)

    In order that the train and man reach the remote end
    of the bridge at the same time,

    $\frac{2x}{s} = \frac{y + 3x}{45}$.   (2)

    Subtracting (2) from (1) yields

    $\frac{x}{s} = \frac{3x}{45}$

    $s = 15.$

    The man must run at 15 mph to 'just' escape the train
    regardless of which end of the bridge he runs to.

15. Since $BC = CB' = 4$, from ship A, the distance that can be seen along ship B's course is $BB' = 8$ miles.

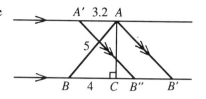

In 24 minutes, A moves to A', a distance of $\frac{24}{60} = 3.2$ miles.

Thus, ship B can only be seen for the distance BB'', a length of $8 - 3.2 = 4.8$ miles.

Since ship B travels the distance BB'' in 24 minutes, its rate is $4.8 \div \frac{60}{24} = 12$ mph.

16. The distance from C to B is

$40 \times \frac{3}{4} = 30$ miles.

$$A \overset{\rule{1.2cm}{0.4pt}}{\underset{m}{}} C \overset{\rule{1.2cm}{0.4pt}}{\underset{30}{}} B$$

Let the distance from A to C be m miles and the rate of the truck from B be r mph.

The times taken by the two trucks to get from their starting points to C are equal.

Thus, $\frac{30}{r} = \frac{m}{40}$

$mr = 1200.$ (1)

Since the truck from B completed the distance from C to A in 20 minutes, we have

$r \times \frac{1}{3} = m$.

Substituting for m in (1) gives

$\frac{1}{3}r^2 = 1200$

$r^2 = 3600$

$r = 60.$

The speed of the other truck is 60 mph.

Sequences and Series

Multiple Choice Questions

1. Since the differences between successive pairs of terms are 1, 2, 4, and 8, a possible difference between the sixth and fifth terms is 16. Thus the sixth term would be $17 + 16 = 33$.
   The answer is E.

2. We could just list the numbers 13, 21, 29, 37, 45, 53, ... , or we could note that the only answer that is 13 more than a multiple of 8 is 53.
   The answer is C.

3. The pattern shown is part of "Pascal's Triangle" which is designed to give the coefficients in the expansion of $(a + b)^n$ where n is a non-negative integer. Each row begins and ends with a 1 and each of the other numbers in the row is obtained by adding the two numbers above it in the preceding row. For example, in the fifth row, the 6 is obtained by adding the two 3s above it.

$$\begin{array}{ccccccccc} & & & & 1 & & & & \\ & & & 1 & & 1 & & & \\ & & 1 & & 2 & & 1 & & \\ & 1 & & 3 & & 3 & & 1 & \\ 1 & & 4 & & 6 & & 4 & & 1 \end{array}$$

   Thus, the second number in the rows after the first row form the sequence
   1, 2, 3, 4, ...
   Hence, the second digit in the fifteenth row is 14.
   The answer is C.

4. Even integers appear only in columns a, c, and e.
   Those in column a are of the form $8t + 2$, $(t = 0, 1, 2, ...)$; those in column e are of the form $8t + 6$; and those in column c are of the form $4t$.
   Since $1000 = 4 \times 250$, it will be in column c.
   The answer is C.

5. Solution 1

   The numbers in the sequence are all multiples of 7.
   The only answer that is a multiple of 7 is 42.
   Solution 2

   If 7 is subtracted n times the resulting number is $N = 777 - 7n$. Since N is divisible by 7 the only possible answer is 42.
   The answer is D.

6. $p - q = (2 + 4 + 6 + ... + 2n) - (1 + 3 + 5 + ... + (2n - 1))$
    $\quad\ = (2 - 1) + (4 - 3) + (6 - 5) + ... + (2n - (2n - 1))$
    $\quad\ =\ \ 1\ \ +\ \ 1\ \ +\ \ 1\ \ + ... +\ \ \ \ 1$
    $\quad\ = n\,.$

    The answer is B.

7. A sequence such as 2, 5, 8, 11, 14, ... , where each number is three greater than the preceding number is called an Arithmetic Sequence. Thus the second term is $2 + 3$, the third term is $2 + 2(3)$, the fourth term is $2 + 3(3)$, and so on. Then the nth term is $2 + (n - 1)3$.

    If the nth term is 11 111, then
    $$2 + (n - 1)3 = 11\ 111$$
    $$3n = 11\ 112$$
    $$n = 3704.$$

    Since 100 numbers are written on each page, 11 111 will be found on page 38.
    The answer is B.

8. Since these are six 10-minute intervals between 4:00 p.m. and 5:00 p.m., the number of cells in the dish at the end of one hour will be $5 \times 2^6 = 320$.
    The answer is A.

9. Solution 1

    Since the difference between successive pairs of terms is 11 and the sequence begins with a 5, then the answer must be 5 more than a multiple of 11. The only answer that satisfies this requirement is 93.

    Solution 2

    Let the terms of the sequence be $t_1, t_2, t_3, ...$.
    Then $t_1 = 5$, $t_2 = 5 + 11$, $t_3 = 5 + 2(11)$, ...
    The nth term is $t_n = 5 + (n - 1)11 = 11n - 6$.
    The only answer of this form is 93, since $93 = 11(9) - 6$.
    The answer is D.

10. Let the second number be x. Then the remaining four numbers are
    $x + 4$, $2x + 4$, $3x + 8$, and $5x + 12$.
    Therefore, $5x + 12 = 47$
    $$5x = 35$$
    $$x = 7.$$
    Hence, $S = 4 + 7 + 11 + 18 + 29 + 47 = 116$.
    The answer is D.

11. The shaded region represents the whole numbers
    from 1 and 50 that are odd and divisible by 7,
    namely the 4 numbers 7, 21, 35, and 49.
    The answer is C.

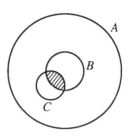

12. Solution 1

    Each number in the sequence leaves remainder 1 on division by 3. The only number
    in the answers which is of this form is 9997.
    Solution 2

    Let the terms of the sequence be $t_1, t_2, t_3, \ldots$.
    Then $t_1 = 1$, $t_2 = 1 + 3$, $t_3 = 1 + 2(3)$, $t_4 = 1 + 3(3), \ldots$.
    The nth term is $t_n = 1 + (n - 1)3 = 3n - 2$.
    Since each term is 2 less than a multiple of 3, the only possible answer is
    $9997 = 3(3333) - 2$.
    The answer is C.

13. Solution 1

    Let the first integer be $2n$ and the fiftieth be $2n + 98$.
    The average of the fifty integers is $\dfrac{2n + (2n + 98)}{2} = 2n + 49$.
    The sum of the fifty integers is $50(2n + 49) = 3250$
    $$2n + 49 = 65$$
    $$2n = 16.$$
    Therefore the largest integer is $2n + 98 = 114$.

    Solution 2
    Let the integers be $2n, 2n + 2, 2n + 4, \ldots, 2n + 98$.
    If the sum of these 50 integers is given by S_{50},
    $S_{50} = 2n + (2n + 2) + (2n + 4) + \ldots + (2n + 98)$,
    or, writing the sum in reverse order, we get
    $S_{50} = (2n + 98) + (2n + 96) + (2n + 94) + \ldots + (2n)$.
    Adding these two sums gives
    $2S_{50} = (4n + 98) + (4n + 98) + (4n + 98) + \ldots + (4n + 98)$
    $\phantom{2S_{50}} = 50(4n + 98)$.
    Therefore $S_{50} = 50(2n + 49) = 3250$
    $$2n + 49 = 65$$
    $$2n + 98 = 114.$$
    The largest integer is 114.
    The answer is D.

Note: the procedure used in Solution 2 can be used to develop a formula for the sum of the arithmetic series $a + (a + d) + (a + 2d) + ... + (a + (n-1)d)$.

14. $1 + \dfrac{1}{2^2} + \dfrac{1}{4^2} + \dfrac{1}{6^2} + \dfrac{1}{8^2} + ...$

$= 1 + \dfrac{1}{2^2}\left[1 + \dfrac{1}{2^2} + \dfrac{1}{3^2} + \dfrac{1}{4^2} + ...\right]$

$= 1 + \dfrac{1}{4}x$.

The answer is C.

15. Let t_k, t_m, and t_n represent the kth, mth, and nth terms respectively.

Then $t_k = a + (k-1)d = m$

and $t_m = a + (m-1)d = k$.

Subtracting the two equations gives

$(k-m)d = m-k$

$d = -1$.

Therefore $a + (k-1)(-1) = m$

$a = m + k - 1$.

$t_n = a + (n-1)d$

$= (m + k - 1) + (n-1)(-1)$

$= m + k - n$.

The answer is A.

16. The sum of the first 4000 natural numbers is

$\dfrac{4000(4001)}{2} = 2000(4001)$.

The sum of the multiples of 5 is

$5 + 10 + 15 + ... + 4000 = 5(1 + 2 + 3 + ... + 800)$

$= \dfrac{5(800)(801)}{2}$

$= 2000(801)$.

The sum of those that are not multiples of 5 is

$2000(4001) - 2000(801) = 2000(3200) = 6\,400\,000$.

The answer is E.

17. In a non-leap year, there are 365 days, which is 52 weeks plus one day.

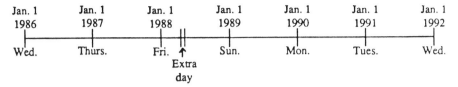

Jan. 1, 1987 occurs on a Thursday and Jan. 1, 1988 occurs on a Friday.

Since 1988 is a leap year, Jan. 1, 1989 occurs on a Sunday.

Then Jan. 1 occurs successively on a Monday, Tuesday, and Wednesday in 1990, 1991, and 1992.

The answer is B.

18. Let $S(n) = \dfrac{6n^5 + an^4 + bn^3 - n}{30}$

Therefore, $S(1) = \dfrac{6 + a + b - 1}{30} = 1^4$

$$a + b = 25. \quad (1)$$

Also, $S(2) = \dfrac{6(2^5) + a(2^4) + b(2^3) - 2}{30} = 1^4 + 2^4$

$$192 + 16a + 8b - 2 = 17(30)$$
$$16a + 8b = 320$$
$$2a + b = 40. \quad (2)$$

Subtracting (1) from (2) gives a = 15.

Thus $b = 10$ and $a - b = 5$.

The answer is D.

19. We must consider four sums in this set of integers, namely the sum of all the integers, the sum of the multiples of 10, the sum of the multiples of 5, and the sum of the multiples of 2. In doing so we can use the formula for the sum of the first k positive integers which is $\dfrac{k(k + 1)}{2}$.

The four sums are:

$$S_1 = 1 + 2 + 3 + \ldots + 10n = \dfrac{10n(10n + 1)}{2}$$
$$= 5n(10n + 1),$$
$$S_2 = 10 + 20 + 30 + \ldots + 10n = 10(1 + 2 + 3 + \ldots + n)$$
$$= \dfrac{10n(n + 1)}{2}$$
$$= 5n(n + 1),$$

$$S_3 = 5 + 10 + 15 + \dots + 10n = 5(1 + 2 + 3 + \dots + 2n)$$
$$= \frac{5(2n)(2n+1)}{2}$$
$$= 5n(2n+1),$$
$$S_4 = 2 + 4 + 6 + \dots + 10n = 2(1 + 2 + 3 + \dots + 5n)$$
$$= \frac{2(5n)(5n+1)}{2}$$
$$= 5n(5n+1).$$

To find the required sum we must calculate $S_1 - S_3 - S_4 + S_2$. (S_2 must be added because the multiples of 10 have been subtracted twice).

$$S_1 - S_3 - S_4 + S_2 = 5n(10n+1) - 5n(2n+1) - 5n(5n+1) + 5n(n+1)$$
$$= 5n[10n + 1 - 2n - 1 - 5n - 1 + n + 1]$$
$$= 5n(4n)$$
$$= 20n^2.$$

The answer is D.

20. $F(60) = 1 + \frac{1}{2} + \frac{1}{3} + \dots + \frac{1}{60}$.

$F(40) = 1 + \frac{1}{2} + \frac{1}{3} + \dots + \frac{1}{40}$.

Therefore, $F(60) - F(40) = \frac{1}{41} + \frac{1}{42} + \frac{1}{43} + \dots + \frac{1}{60}$.

To obtain a lower bound for $F(60) - F(40)$ we can replace each denominator by 60.

Therefore, $F(60) - F(40) > \frac{1}{60} + \frac{1}{60} + \frac{1}{60} + \dots + \frac{1}{60} = \frac{20}{60} = \frac{1}{3}$.

To obtain an upper bound for $F(60) - F(40)$ we can replace each denominator by 40.

Thus, $F(60) - F(40) < \frac{1}{40} + \frac{1}{40} + \frac{1}{40} + \dots + \frac{1}{40} = \frac{20}{40} = \frac{1}{2}$.

Therefore, $\frac{1}{3} < (F(60) - F(40)) < \frac{1}{2}$.

The answer is B.

Full Solution Questions

1. The bottom rows of the patterns representing triangular numbers contain 1, 2, 3, 4, ... circles. Hence, the bottom row of the seventh triangle number has 7 circles and the number is $7 + 6 + 5 + 4 + 3 + 2 + 1 = 28$.

2. The pattern of numbers of letters in the columns is 1, 3, 5, 7, 9, ... The nth column would have $2n - 1$ members. Since K is the eleventh letter, there will be 21 letters in its column.

3. The successive differences between terms are 1, 3, 5, 7, ... Thus the next two differences could be 9 and 11, giving the terms 26 and 37.

4. Since the one sequence increases by 5 and the other by 7, the common terms will occur after an interval of 35.
    Since the common entry occurs at 17, the next would occur at 35 + 17 = 52 and the following at 52 + 35 = 87, etc.

5. The first number is 7, which is 6 less than a multiple of 13.
    Each number is of the form $13n - 6$, where n is a positive integer.
    If 72 is counted it will happen when $13n - 6 = 72$
    $$13n = 78$$
    $$n = 6.$$
    Therefore, 72 is the sixth term in the sequence, and thus will be counted.

6. Solution 1
    The sum can be written as
    $1 + 3 + 5 + 7 + \cdots + 93 + 95 + 97 + 99$
    $= (1 + 99) + (3 + 97) + (5 + 95) + ... + (49 + 51)$
    $= 100 + 100 + 100 + ... + 100$
    $= 25(100)$
    $= 2500.$
    Solution 2
    Intuitively, we can find the sum by considering partial sums.
    $1 = 1^2$
    $1 + 3 = 2^2$
    $1 + 3 + 5 = 3^2$
    .
    .
    .

    $1 + 3 + 5 + ... + 99 = 50^2 = 2500.$
    While this is not a proof, it can be shown that the sum of the first n odd integers is always equal to n^2.

7. The total number of blocks is
    $9 + 8 + 7 + 6 + 5 + 4 + 3 + 2 + 1 = 45.$

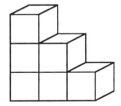

8. The number of integers used in the first 60 rows is
    $1 + 2 + 3 + 4 + ... + 57 + 58 + 59 + 60$
    $= (1 + 60) + (2 + 59) + (3 + 58) + ... + (30 + 31)$
    $= (61)(30)$
    $= 1830.$
    The first entry in the sixty-first row is
    $\qquad 1830 + 1 = 1831.$
    The twenty-third entry in this row is
    $\qquad 1830 + 23 = 1853.$

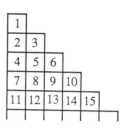

9. The sum of the first 30 natural numbers is $\dfrac{(30)(31)}{2} = (15)(31) = 465.$

10. The total amount was $1 + 2 + 4 + 8 + 16 + 32 + 64 + 128 = 255$ dollars.

11. Since there was one gallon of bacteria at 2:00 p.m. and the number doubles each minute, there was $\dfrac{1}{2}$ gallon at 1:59 and $\dfrac{1}{4}$ gallon or 1 quart of bacteria at 1:58.

12. The pattern $-2, -1, 0, 1, 2$ repeats every fifth entry.
    Since the 5th, 10th, 15th, etc. terms of the sequence are all 2, the 1985th term is 2.
    Therefore, the 1987th term is -1.

13. Since the 24th day of June is Thursday, the 17th, 10th, and 3rd days were also Thursdays.
    Hence, the first of June was a Tuesday.

14. The weekly heights of the first plant form the sequence 12, 14, 16, 18, 20, ...
    The weekly heights of the second plant form the sequence 3, 8, 13, 18, 23, ...
    They reach the same height, 18 cm, in 3 weeks.

15. The sequence of steps taken to reach the tree is 2, –1, 2, –1, 2, –1, 2, –1, 2, –1, 2.
    The sum of these terms is 7 but the total number of steps is $6 \times 2 + 5 \times 1 = 17.$

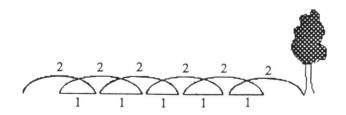

16. Since the sum of two consecutive positive integers is odd, they cannot add to 1000. If n, $n + 1$, and $n + 2$ are three consecutive positive integers whose sum is 1000, then $3n + 3 = 1000$, $3n = 997$, and $n = 332\frac{1}{3}$ which is not an integer.

If n, $n + 1$, $n + 2$, and $n + 3$ are four consecutive positive integers whose sum is 1000, then $4n + 6 = 1000$, $4n = 994$ and $n = 238\frac{1}{2}$ which is not an integer.

However, five consecutive positive integers, n, $n + 1$, $n + 2$, $n + 3$, and $n + 4$ can add to 1000 since $5n + 10 = 1000$ gives $5n = 990$ or $n = 198$.

The five consecutive positive integers are 198, 199, 200, 201, and 202, and their sum is 1000.

17. Rewrite the series $\dfrac{1}{(2)(3)} + \dfrac{1}{(3)(4)} + \dfrac{1}{(4)(5)} + \ldots + \dfrac{1}{(61)(62)}$ in the form

$$\left(\frac{1}{2} - \frac{1}{3}\right) + \left(\frac{1}{3} - \frac{1}{4}\right) + \left(\frac{1}{4} - \frac{1}{5}\right) + \ldots + \left(\frac{1}{61} - \frac{1}{62}\right)$$

$$= \frac{1}{2} - \frac{1}{3} + \frac{1}{3} - \frac{1}{4} + \frac{1}{4} - \frac{1}{5} + \ldots + \frac{1}{61} - \frac{1}{62}$$

$$= \frac{1}{2} - \frac{1}{62}$$

$$= \frac{30}{62}$$

$$= \frac{15}{31}.$$

Since 15 and 31 are relatively prime $a = 15$ and $b = 31$.

Therefore, $a + b = 46$.

18. Solution 1

Since $f(3n) = n + f(3n - 3)$, then $f(3n) - f(3n - 3) = n$.

Set $n = 7, 6, 5, 4, 3, 2$:

$$f(21) - f(18) = 7$$
$$f(18) - f(15) = 6$$
$$f(15) - f(12) = 5$$
$$f(12) - f(9) \ = 4$$
$$f(9) \ - f(6) \ = 3$$
$$f(6) \ - f(3) \ = 2.$$

Add: $f(21) - f(3) \ = 27$.

Therefore, $f(21) = 27 + 1 = 28$.

<u>Solution 2</u>

$f(21) = 7 + f(3 \times 6)$ and since $f(3 \times 6) = 6 + f(3 \times 5)$,

$f(21) = 7 + 6 + f(3 \times 5)$

$\qquad = 7 + 6 + 5 + f(3 \times 4)$

$\qquad = 7 + 6 + 5 + 4 + f(3 \times 3)$

$\qquad = 7 + 6 + 5 + 4 + 3 + f(3 \times 2)$

$\qquad = 7 + 6 + 5 + 4 + 3 + 2 + f(3 \times 1)$

$\qquad = 7 + 6 + 5 + 4 + 3 + 2 + 1$

$\qquad = 28.$

19. Since $f(n + 1) = \dfrac{2f(n) + 1}{2} = f(n) + \dfrac{1}{2}$,

    then $f(n + 1) - f(n) = \dfrac{1}{2}$.

    Substitute $n = 234, 233, \ldots, 2, 1$ in this formula.

    $f(235) - f(234) = \dfrac{1}{2}$

    $f(234) - f(233) = \dfrac{1}{2}$

    $f(233) - f(232) = \dfrac{1}{2}$

    .
    .
    .

    $f(2) - f(1) = \dfrac{1}{2}$.

    Adding, we get

    $f(235) - f(1) = 234\left(\dfrac{1}{2}\right) = 117.$

    But $f(1) = 1$, and so $f(235) = 118.$

3-Dimensional Problems

Multiple Choice Questions

1. If the figure is rotated through 180° in a counterclockwise direction, the figure in (A) is obtained.
    The answer is A.

2. The volume of the original cube is $l \times w \times h$.
    The volume of larger cube is
    $(2l)(2w)(2h) = 8lwh$.
    Therefore 8 original cubes will fill the larger cube.
    The answer is D.

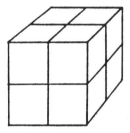

3. The top surface is illustrated (12 cubes are visible). Each edge cube has more than one red face. Hence only the two central cubes have exactly one red face. Similarly, there are 2 central cubes on the bottom surface having exactly one red face.
    There are no such cubes on the other four faces.
    Hence the total is 4.
    The answer is B.

4. On each of the six faces of the original block there will be a quadrilateral shaped face of P.
    If each of the eight corners of the block is removed a triangular face of P will remain. Therefore P will have $6 + 8 = 14$ faces.
    The six quadrilateral faces of P have a total of 24 edges and these include all the edges of the triangular faces.
    Therefore the sum of the number of edges and the number of faces is
    $24 + 14 = 38$.
    The answer is B.

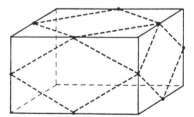

5. The volume of water in the pail is $(\pi \times 13^2 \times 30)$ cm³.

    If the depth of water in the fish tank is d cm, then $52 \times 39 \times d = \pi \times 13^2 \times 30$.

    $$d = \frac{\pi \times 13^2 \times 30}{52 \times 39} = \frac{5\pi}{2} \text{ cm.}$$

    The answer is B.

6. The diagrams show the bowl in cross-section, first
    in normal position, then tilted.
    From the first we obtain $OB = 8$ and $OC = 4$.
    Hence $CB = \sqrt{64 - 16} = 4\sqrt{3}$.
    If the angle of the tilt in the second diagram is
    $\angle OA_1C_1$, then $OC_1 = 4$ and $A_1C_1 = 4\sqrt{3}$.
    Then $OA_1 = \sqrt{16 + 48} = 8$.
    Hence $\angle OA_1C_1 = 30°$.

    The answer is B.

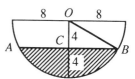
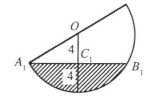

7. If plane p is drawn through the
    middle of the cube parallel to the
    base, then one-half of the
    octahedron is above p and one-
    half below p, and each half is a
    regular pyramid.
    Since $\sqrt{\frac{1}{4} + \frac{1}{4}} = \frac{1}{\sqrt{2}}$, each
    pyramid has a square base with
    side length $\frac{1}{\sqrt{2}}$.
    Since the height is $\frac{1}{2}$, the volume
    of the pyramid is $\frac{1}{3}\left(\frac{1}{\sqrt{2}}\right)^2 \frac{1}{2} = \frac{1}{12}$.
    The volume of the octahedron is $\frac{1}{6}$.
    The answer is D.

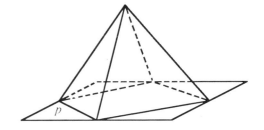

8. The original volume is $\frac{4}{3}\pi r^3$.

    Since the new radius is $2r$, the new volume is $\frac{4}{3}\pi(2r)^3$.

    The ratio of new to old volume is $\dfrac{\frac{4}{3}\pi (2r)^3}{\frac{4}{3}\pi r^3} = \frac{8}{1}$.

    The answer is D.

9. Let *ST* represent the reed. We are given that
    $ST = SU$ and the radius of the pond, *OU*, is 4
    feet.
    If *d* is the pond depth,
    then $OS = d$ and $SU = d + 1$.
    Then, from $\triangle OUS$, $(d + 1)^2 = 4^2 + d^2$
    $$2d + 1 = 16$$
    $$d = \frac{15}{2} .$$
    The pond is $\frac{15}{2}$ feet deep.
    The answer is A.

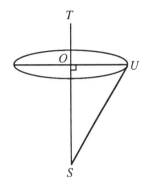

10. Flatten the block so that its surface
    is in one plane, as illustrated.
    The shortest distance from *A* to *B*
    is the hypotenuse of right-angled
    triangle *ABC*.
    $AB = \sqrt{8^2 + 6^2} = 10$.
    The answer is E.

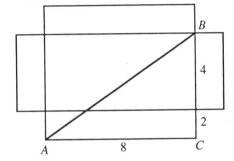

11. The length of wire necessary for one wrap is the
    diagonal of a rectangle of length equal to the
    circumference of the cylinder and height equal to
    one-tenth the cylinder's height.
    Hence the length of wire necessary for ten wraps is
    the diagonal of the rectangle of length equal to ten
    times the circumference of the cylinder and height
    equal to the height of the cylinder.
    The length of this rectangle is
    $10(10\pi) = 100\pi$ cm and its height is 10 cm.
    The length of the diagonal is $\sqrt{(100\pi)^2 + 10^2}$
    $$= 10\sqrt{100\pi^2 + 1} \text{ cm}.$$
    The answer is A.

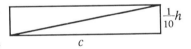

12. If the cube has side *x*, its surface area is $6x^2$.
    The new cube will have side $x + 1.5x = 2.5x$, and surface area $6(2.5x)^2 = 37.5x^2$.
    This is an increase of $31.5x^2$.
    The percent increase is $\frac{31.5x^2}{6x^2} = 5.25 = 525\%$.
    The answer is C.

13. The original volume is rst.
    The new volumes possible are
    $$(r + 1)st \quad = rst + st,$$
    $$r(s + 1)t \quad = rst + rt,$$
    and $rs(t + 1) \quad = rst + rs.$
    Since $r < s < t$, then $rst + st$ is the greatest.
    The answer is A.

14. The height of the top part is $\frac{1}{3}h$.
    The area of the base of the top part is $\frac{1}{9}A$.
    The volume of the top is $\frac{1}{3}(\frac{1}{9}A)(\frac{1}{3}h) = \frac{1}{81}Ah$.
    Therefore the volume of the remaining part is
    $\frac{1}{3}Ah - \frac{1}{81}Ah = \frac{26}{81}Ah.$.
    The answer is E.

15. Let each edge of the large cube be 2 units. Then each edge of the smaller cubes is 1 unit.
    The surface area of the larger cube is $6 \times 2 \times 2 = 24$ square units.
    The total surface area of the 8 smaller cubes is $8 \times 6 \times 1 \times 1 = 48$ square units, which is double that of the large cube.
    The answer is C.

16. If the sum of the numbers on three of the faces is 15, the numbers are 4, 5, and 6. If the sum of the numbers on three of the faces is 14, the numbers are 3, 5, and 6. There are two cases to consider. In each case both the 5 and 6 must be visible from two positions.

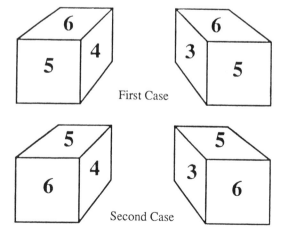

First Case

Second Case

If the 6 is on the top (Case 1), then 1 and 2 must be on the sides to give a sum of 9.
This is not possible since three of the four sides are already allocated to 3, 4, and 5.
Hence the number on the top is 5 (Case 2) and 1 is on the fourth side since
$5 + 3 + 1 = 9$.
Therefore the bottom number is 2.
The answer is B.

Full Solution Questions

1. In the diagram, there are three edges enclosing each
    of the top and bottom faces. There are three vertical
    edges. The total number of edges is 9.

    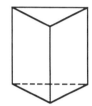

2. The middle cube on each edge will have exactly two
    painted faces. Since there are twelve edges, there
    are 12 cubes with exactly two painted faces.

    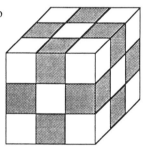

3. Solution 1
    Since each face of a cube shares an edge with four other faces, only opposite faces can
    be the same colour. Hence the minimum number of colours required is 3.

    Solution 2
    In tackling problems such as this, a diagram
    always helps. The difficulty is in drawing a 3-
    dimensional figure in two dimensions and
    showing all of its faces. The diagram shown is
    one way to represent a cube in two dimensions.
    B and C represent the top and bottom of the
    cube and K, L, M, and N represent the sides.
    B and C share no common edge. Similarly, K
    and M share no common edge, and L and N
    share no common edge. Therefore the cube can
    be painted using a minimum of three colours.

    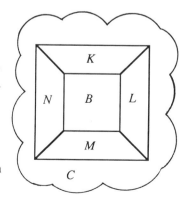

4. The volume of the first box is $9 \times 6 \times 24$ cm^3.

    If the second box has height h, then its volume is $6 \times 4h$ cm^3.

    Hence $6 \times 4h = \dfrac{1}{2}(9 \times 6 \times 24)$

    $$h = \frac{1}{2}\left(\frac{9 \times 6 \times 24}{6 \times 4}\right) = 27.$$

    The height of the box is 27 cm.

5. If the circular base of the cone has radius r, then its
    circumference is $2\pi r$.

    But when the cone is cut along its slant height S
    and opened out, it forms a semicircle of radius 10,
    and hence the arc length of the semicircle is 10π,
    which is equal to the circumference of the base.

    Thus, $2\pi r = 10\pi$

    $r = 5$.

    Now, $h^2 + r^2 = S^2$.

    $$h = \sqrt{100 - 25} = 5\sqrt{3}.$$

    The height of the cone is $5\sqrt{3}$ cm.

    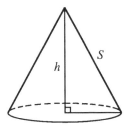

6. In the diagram, $AB = 1$, $BE = 2$, $BC = 3$.

    Since $\triangle ADC$ is right-angled, $AD^2 = DC^2 + AC^2$.

    $\triangle ABC$ is also right-angled.

    Hence, $AC^2 = AB^2 + BC^2$.

    Therefore $AD^2 = DC^2 + AB^2 + BC^2$

    $$= 2^2 + 1^2 + 3^2$$
    $$= 14.$$

    The diagonal is $\sqrt{14}$ inches.

    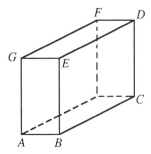

7. Since each vertex of the cube touches the sphere,
    the diagonal of the cube is equal to the diameter
    of the sphere.

    If each side of the cube is x cm, then the

    diagonal of a face is $\sqrt{x^2 + x^2} = \sqrt{2}\,x$ cm.

    Hence the diagonal of the cube is

    $\sqrt{2x^2 + x^2} = \sqrt{3}\,x$ cm.

    Now, $\sqrt{3}\,x = 12$

    $3x = 12\sqrt{3}$

    $x = 4\sqrt{3}$.

    Therefore the volume of the cube is $(4\sqrt{3})^3 = 192\sqrt{3}$ cm^3.

    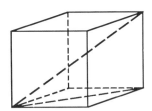

8. Let the depth of the water before freezing be h cm.
   Since the water cannot expand horizontally, all expansion is vertical.
   Therefore $1.1\,h = 38.5$
   $$h = 35.$$
   The container should be filled to a depth of 35 cm.

9. The volume of the water is $4^2 \times 3 = 48$ cu. ft.
   The volume of the cube is $2^3 = 8$ cu. ft.
   Hence the total volume is 56 cu. ft.
   If h is the new height, then the combined volume is

   $4^2 h = 56$
   $$h = \frac{56}{16} = 3\frac{1}{2}.$$
   The new height of the water is $3\frac{1}{2}$ feet.

10. Let one side of the original square be x feet, or
    $12x$ inches.
    Then the volume of the box is $6(12x - 12)^2$.
    Therefore, $6(12x - 12)^2 = 864$
    $$12^2 (x - 1)^2 = 144$$
    $$(x - 1)^2 = 1$$
    $$x = 2, \quad \text{since } x - 1 > 0.$$
    The original square had an area of 4 square feet.

    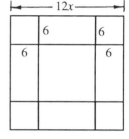

11. The bottom requires $10 \times 10 = 100$ cubes. The
    construction of one layer of the four sides requires
    $2 \times 10 + 2 \times 8 = 36$ cubes.
    Since there are nine layers, the total number of
    cubes is $(9 \times 36) + 100 = 424$.

    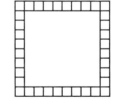

12. Since the width, 60 cm, is the same for both
    positions of the tank, only the cross-sectional
    areas need be considered.
    Since $AD = 40$ cm and $AC = 50$ cm, the area of
    $\triangle ADC$ is $\frac{1}{2}(40)(50) = 1000$ cm^2.

    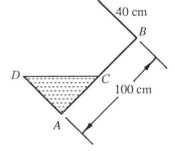

When the tank is returned to a horizontal
position its depth, d, can be obtained
using the fact that $100d = 1000$.
Therefore $d = 10$.

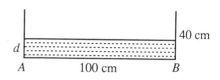

The depth is 10 cm when the tank is in
the horizontal position.

13. The required section, $ABCD$, is a tetrahedron.
The volume of a tetrahedron is

$$\frac{1}{3}(\text{area of base})(\text{height}).$$

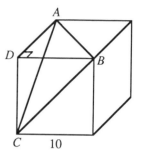

Any one of the triangles ABD, ADC, BDC,
ABC can be considered as base, but using $\triangle ABC$
makes the problem much more difficult than is
necessary.

The area of base $\triangle ABD$ is $\frac{1}{2} \times 10 \times 10 = 50$.

The height of the tetrahedron from this base is 10.
Therefore the volume of the smaller section is

$$\frac{1}{3}(50)(10) = 166\frac{2}{3}.$$

14. The centres of the 4 spheres form a regular
tetrahedron $ABCD$, each of whose edges is 2.
If EC is a median of face BCD, then $BE = 1$
and $EC = \sqrt{3}$.

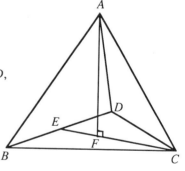

If $AF \perp EC$, then F is the centroid of face BCD,
so $FC = \frac{2}{3}EC = \frac{2\sqrt{3}}{3}$.

Thus $AF = \sqrt{(AC)^2 - (FC)^2}$

$$= \sqrt{4 - \frac{4}{3}}$$

$$= \sqrt{\frac{8}{3}}$$

$$= \frac{2\sqrt{2}}{\sqrt{3}}.$$

Since plane BCD is 1 unit above the level surface
and A is 1 unit below the highest point of the top
sphere, then the distance from the level surface to
this highest point is $1 + 1 + \frac{2\sqrt{2}}{\sqrt{3}} = 2 + \frac{2\sqrt{2}}{\sqrt{3}}$.

15. The volume of the cone is $\frac{1}{3}\pi (30)^2 (100)$.

    When the cone is completely immersed, the water level has risen a distance x cm such that the column of water with base having diameter 120 cm and height x cm has volume equal to that of the cone.

    Thus, $\pi(60)^2 (x) = \frac{1}{3}\pi (30)^2 (100)$
    $$x = \frac{25}{3} = 8\frac{1}{3}.$$
    Therefore the cone is lowered $100 - 8\frac{1}{3} = 91\frac{2}{3}$ cm.

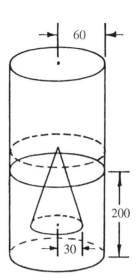

16. The diagram represents a cross-section of the tank.
    $$AB = 2BD = 2\sqrt{2^2 - 1^2}$$
    $$= 2\sqrt{3}$$
    Then the surface area of the gasoline is the area of a rectangle of dimensions 16 by $2\sqrt{3}$, or $32\sqrt{3}$ square feet.

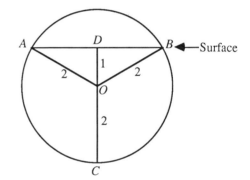

17. There are six square faces and eight triangular faces. Each square face is one-half the area of a face of the original cube. The area of these six faces is $\frac{1}{2} \times 6 \times 4^2 = 48$.

    Each triangular face is an equilateral triangle with sides $\sqrt{2^2 + 2^2} = 2\sqrt{2}$.

    The height h is determined by
    $$h^2 = 8 - 2 = 6$$
    $$h = \sqrt{6}.$$
    Hence the area of the eight triangles is
    $$8 \times \frac{1}{2} \times 2\sqrt{2} \times \sqrt{6} = 16\sqrt{3}.$$
    The total surface area is $48 + 16\sqrt{3}$.

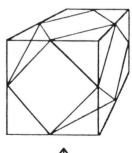

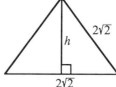

Rectilinear Figures

Multiple Choice Questions

1. The length of each side is $\dfrac{6 + 10 + 11}{3} = 9$.
    The answer is B.

2. Complete the rectangle as shown.
    The perimeter of the given shape is equal to
    the perimeter of the rectangle, which is
    $\qquad 2(5w + 5h) = 10w + 10h$.
    The answer is B.

3. Let the width of the rectangle be W.
    Then $W = \dfrac{A}{L}$, and hence the perimeter is $2L + 2W = 2L + \dfrac{2A}{L}$.
    The answer is D.

4. The required area is equal to the area of rectangle
    $ABCD$ minus the area of triangle EFD.
    The area of $\triangle EFD$ is $\dfrac{1}{2}(6)(3) = 9$.
    The area of the figure is $10 \times 5 - 9 = 41$.
    The answer is C.

    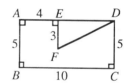

5. The area of trapezoid $ABCF$ is $\dfrac{1}{2}(12 + 3)\,AF$.

    The area of trapezoid $FCDE$ is $\dfrac{1}{2}(12 + 3)\,FE$.

    The area of pentagon $ABCDE$ is

    $\dfrac{1}{2}(12 + 3)(AF + FE) = \dfrac{1}{2}(15)(16)$

    $\qquad\qquad\qquad\qquad\quad = 120$.

    The answer is A.

    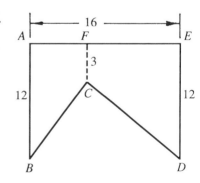

6. Solution 1
    The area of the original rectangle is $24 \times 15 = 360$ cm².
    If x is the increase in width, then
    $$(24 - 6)(15 + x) = 360$$
    $$18(15 + x) = 360$$
    $$18x = 90$$
    $$x = 5.$$
    The increase in width is 5 cm.

    Solution 2

    The area of the original rectangle is 24×15.
    The length of the adjusted rectangle is 18 and its width is w.
    Hence $18w = 24 \times 15$
    $$w = \frac{24 \times 15}{18} = 20.$$
    The width must be increased by 5 cm.
    The answer is B.

7. Since the triangle is right-angled, we can
    express its area in two ways
    $$\frac{1}{2}(25)(h) = \frac{1}{2}(15)(20)$$
    $$h = \frac{(15)(20)}{25} = 12.$$
    The answer is B.

    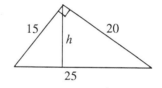

8. Draw the rhombus as shown.
    Rhombus $OABC = 2 \triangle OAB$.
    But $OA = 8 = OB$, so $\triangle OAB$ is
    equilateral, and $\angle AOB = 60°$.
    Hence $OD: AD: OA = 1: \sqrt{3}: 2$.
    Thus $OD = 4$ and $AD = 4\sqrt{3}$.
    $$2\triangle OAB = 2\left(\frac{1}{2}\right)(OB)(AD)$$
    $$= 8(4\sqrt{3})$$
    $$= 32\sqrt{3}.$$
    The answer is B.

    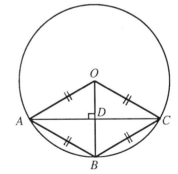

9. If the height of the second box is h, its volume is $6 \times 4 \times h$.
    Therefore $6 \times 4 \times h = \frac{1}{2}(9 \times 6 \times 24)$
    $$h = 27.$$
    The height of the box is 27 cm.
    The answer is C.

10. The area of the figure is the sum of the area of the square and four times the area of any one triangle.

    In the triangle the base is $2x$.

    If h is the height, then

    $$h^2 + x^2 = 4x^2$$
    $$h = \sqrt{3}x.$$

    The required area is $4x^2 + 4\left[\frac{1}{2}(2x)(\sqrt{3}x)\right]$
    $$= 4x^2 + 4\sqrt{3}x^2$$
    $$= 4(1+\sqrt{3})x^2.$$

    The answer is A.

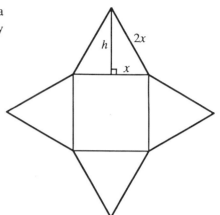

11. The line segments AOD and BOC divide the square into 4 equal smaller squares. Half of each, namely triangles UAB, VAC, CWD, DZB, is wasted.

    The answer is B.

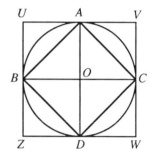

12. Divide the figure into three parts as shown.

    The area is $x^2 + 2hx = 60$
    $$h = \frac{60 - x^2}{2x}.$$

    As x increases, h decreases.

    For $x = 3$, $h = \frac{51}{6} = \frac{17}{2} = 8.5$.

    For $x = 5$, $h = \frac{35}{10} = 3.5$.

    Hence, if $3 < x < 5$, then $3.5 < h < 8.5$.

    The answer is B.

13. The width of the rectangle obtained by folding the square is one-half its length. Since the perimeter of the rectangle is 18 cm, its length and width are 6 cm and 3 cm, respectively.

    Therefore the area of the square is $6 \times 6 = 36$ cm^2.

    The answer is E.

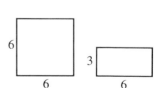

14. Let the sides have lengths ak and bk, $(a > b)$.

Therefore $2ak + 2bk = x$.

Thus $k = \dfrac{x}{2a + 2b}$, and hence the shorter side has length $\dfrac{bx}{2a + 2b}$.

The answer is E.

15. The area of parallelogram *DEBF* is

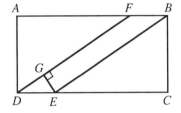

$$(DE)\,(AD) = 12$$
$$6\,DE = 12$$
$$DE = 2.$$

Hence $EC = 10$

and $EB = \sqrt{10^2 + 6^2} = \sqrt{136} = 2\sqrt{34}.$

Then the area of parallelogram *DEBF* is

$(EB)\,(EG) = 12.$

$$EG = \frac{6}{\sqrt{34}} = \frac{6\sqrt{34}}{34} = \frac{3\sqrt{34}}{17}.$$

The answer is A.

16. Draw perpendiculars *DX* and *DY* as shown.

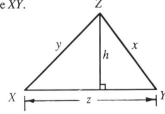

Then $\triangle DXE \equiv \triangle DYG$ because $DX = DY$,

$\angle GDY = \angle EDX$, and $\angle DXE = \angle DYG$.

Therefore, area *DEFG* = area *DXFY*

$$= \tfrac{1}{4}(9)$$
$$= 2.25.$$

The answer is B.

17. The shortest altitude is drawn to the longest side *XY*.

Hence the area of triangle *XYZ* is $A = \tfrac{1}{2}zh.$

Therefore, $h = \dfrac{2A}{z}.$

The answer is D.

18. The total area of the four shaded triangles is
$$\tfrac{1}{2}\left[\left(4\times3\right)+\left(4\times3\right)+\left(3\times2\right)+\left(5\times2\right)\right]=20.$$

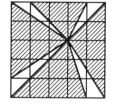

Since the area of the square is 25, the unshaded area is $25-20=5$.

The ratio of the shaded area to the unshaded area is $20:5=4:1$.

The answer is A.

19. For any value of x,
$$(2x-5)<(2x+2)<(2x+3).$$
Hence $2x+3$ is the length of the hypotenuse and the sides around the right angle have lengths $(2x-5)$ and $(2x+2)$.

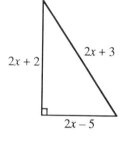

The area of the triangle is $\tfrac{1}{2}(2x+2)(2x-5)$, which simplifies to $2x^2-3x-5$.

The answer is C.

20. Draw $EF\perp AB$, and let $EF=h$.

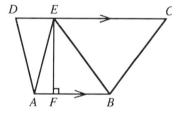

The area of the trapezoid is $\tfrac{1}{2}(AB+CD)\,h$.
$$18=\tfrac{1}{2}(4+CD)\,h$$

Therefore $h\,(4+CD)=36$.

Since $4+CD$ is greater than 4, the only possibilities, using integers, for h and $(4+CD)$, are $(1,36)$, $(2,18)$, $(3,12)$, $(4,9)$, $(6,6)$.

But CD is an odd integer, so $4+CD$ is also odd. The only acceptable pair of those listed has $h=4$, $(4+CD)=9$.

Hence the area of $\triangle EAB=\tfrac{1}{2}(4)(4)=8$.

The answer is D.

21. Let the length of each side of square $EFGH$ be x.
    Then $AD = x + 2$ and $PH = x - 1$.
    Since the area of rectangle $ABCD$ equals the area
    of square $EFGH$,

    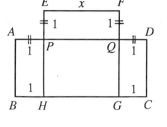

    $$(x + 2)(x - 1) = x^2$$
    $$x^2 + x - 2 = x^2$$
    $$x = 2.$$
    Therefore $BC = BH + HG + GC$
    $$= 1 + 2 + 1$$
    $$= 4.$$
    The answer is C.

22. Since $AB = EH = 2 + 5 + 3 = 10$ and
    $AD = 2 + 3 = 5$, the area of $ABCD$ is
    $5 \times 10 = 50$.
    Hence the shaded area is $50 - 4 - 9 = 37$.
    The answer is D.

    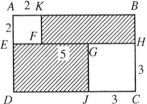

23. Since the perimeter is $2(l + w)$, we have
    $$2y + 4 = 2(y + w)$$
    $$w = 2.$$
    The area is $2y$.
    The answer is A.

24. Solution 1
    The area of $ABCD$ equals the area of rectangle
    $PQRS$ minus the sum of the areas of triangles
    $PAB, ASD, BQC,$ and DCR.
    The area of $ABCD$ is
    $$6 \times 5 - \frac{1}{2}\left[(4 \times 4) + (1 \times 1) + (2 \times 2) + (3 \times 5)\right] = 12.$$

    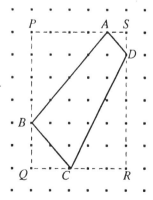

    Solution 2
    Pick's Theorem states that the area of a polygon P
    with lattice points as vertices is given by
    $$A = \frac{1}{2}e + i - 1,$$
    where e is the number of lattice points lying on the
    edges of P and i is the number of lattice points
    lying inside P.
    Therefore the area of $ABCD$ is $\frac{1}{2}(8) + 9 - 1 = 12$.

[You may be interested in investigating Pick's
Theorem in your school library.]
The answer is E.

25. Since $\triangle AD'K$ is the image of $\triangle ADK$, then
$AD' = 10$ and $DK = D'K = x$.
In $\triangle ABD'$, $BD' = \sqrt{100 - 64} = 6$.
Therefore $D'C = 4$.
In $\triangle D'KC$, $x^2 - (8 - x)^2 = 16$
$$x^2 - 64 + 16x - x^2 = 16$$
$$16x = 80$$
$$x = 5.$$
Therefore $DK = 5$.
The answer is A.

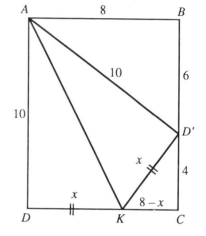

Full Solution Questions

1. The path consists of downward,
    horizontal, and upward steps. The
    downward and upward steps have total
    lengths equal to PS and RQ
    respectively. The horizontal steps have
    total length equal to SR.
    Hence the path length is
    $12 + 16 + 12 = 40$ units.

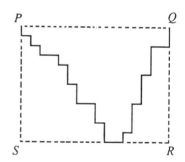

2. Square $ABCD$ and triangle AEB have the same
    base AB, and the same altitude AD.
    Since the square has sides of length 6, the area of
    the triangle is $\frac{1}{2}(6^2) = 18$.

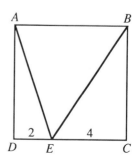

3. There are 17 tiles and the perimeter includes two sides from 15 of them. The two tiles at the ends contribute three sides to the perimeter.

   Hence the perimeter is $(15 \times 2) + (2 \times 3) = 36$.

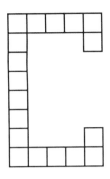

4. If each of the equal sides is x cm, the third side is $(x - 5)$ cm.
   Then $x + x + x - 5 = 31$
   $$x = 12.$$
   Each of the equal sides is 12 cm.

5. If the floor dimensions are doubled, then the floor area is quadrupled.
   Hence 12 litres of paint are required.

6. The path consists of upward, horizontal, and downward distances.

   The sum of the upward distances is $4 \times 2 = 8$.
   The sum of the downward distances is also 8.
   The sum of the horizontal distances is $4 \times 8 = 32$.
   The length of the path is 48.

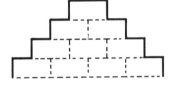

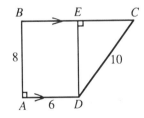

7. <u>Solution 1</u>
   $ABCD$ is a trapezoid.
   Its area is $\frac{1}{2}(12 + 6)\, 8 = 72$.

   <u>Solution 2</u>
   Draw DE perpendicular to BC.
   The area of rectangle $BEDA$ is $8 \times 6 = 48$.
   The area of triangle ECD is $\frac{1}{2}(12 - 6)\, 8 = 24$.
   The area of the figure is 72.

8. Draw XEY parallel to BC. Then $AX = DY = 4$.
   Triangle AXE is a right-angled triangle with
   $AX = 4$ and $AE = 5$, so $XE = 3$. Similarly
   $EY = 3$.
   The areas of triangles AXE and DEY are each
   $\frac{1}{2}(4)(3) = 6$.
   Rectangle $XBCY$ has area $4 \times 6 = 24$.
   The area of the figure is 36.

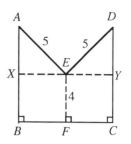

9. The area of the larger square is $(2n + 1)^2$ and the area of the smaller square is $(2n)^2$.
   The difference in area is $(2n + 1)^2 - (2n)^2 = (4n + 1)(1) = 4n + 1$.

10. Label the diagram as shown, with BC extended to
    meet HG at X and FG extended to meet CD at Y.
    The areas of rectangles $ABXH$ and $YDEF$ are each
    $6 \times 8 = 48$.
    Let CY be t units, so that the area of $CYGX$ is $3t$.
    Then $3t + (2 \times 48) = 108$
    $$3t = 12$$
    $$t = 4.$$
    The perimeter of the figure is $2(6 + 8 + 6 + 5 + 4) = 58$.

11. The lengths of the two pieces of wire are 40 cm and 20 cm.
    The sides of the squares they form have lengths 10 cm and 5 cm respectively.
    Then the total area of the two squares is $10^2 + 5^2 = 125$ cm^2.

12. The path length horizontally is $40 + 20 = 60$ m.
    The bottom corridor width is $(5 + 8) - 10 = 3$ m.
    The vertical path is $13 - \frac{1}{2}(5 + 3) = 9$ m.
    The total path length is 69 m.

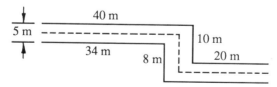

13. The area of $\triangle ABC$ is $\frac{1}{2}AD \times BC = 3BC = 24$

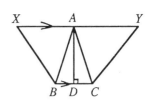

square inches.
Therefore $BC = 8$ inches.

The area of trapezoid $BXYC$ is $\frac{1}{2}(XY + BC)AD$

$$= \frac{1}{2}(28)(6)$$

$$= 84 \text{ square inches.}$$

14. The area of $\triangle ABC$ is $\frac{1}{2}bh = 12$.

$$bh = 24.$$

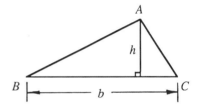

Since both b and h are integers, each must divide 24. Also h is an odd integer
greater than 1 and the only such integer which divides 24 is 3. Hence $h = 3$.
Therefore $3b = 24$
$$b = 8.$$
The base is 8.

15. From the given information, $PA = 10$, $AB = 4$,
$BQ = 9$, and $PQ = 23$. If PQ is to be 21, then
AB must be 2 and the square on AB must be 4, a
decrease of 12.

16. In the diagram, draw line segments AX and BY
as shown.
Then $\triangle ADX \equiv \triangle BCY$ since $AD = BC$ and
corresponding sides are parallel.
Hence $BY = AX = PQ = 5$,
and $BR = YS = CS - CY$
$$= CS - DX$$
$$= 10 - 4$$
$$= 6.$$

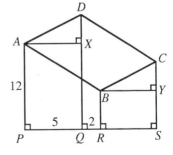

The area of trapezoid $BRSC$ is $\frac{1}{2}(BR + CS)BY$

$$= \frac{1}{2}(6 + 10)\,5$$

$$= 40.$$

17. The area of the picture and the pad is $ab + cd$.

    The area of the entire calendar is $2ab + 2cd$.

    The width of the calendar is $\dfrac{2ab + 2cd}{h}$.

18. If the square has side x, then its area is x^2.

    The triangle has base $4x$ and its area is also x^2.

    If the triangle's altitude is h,

    then $\dfrac{1}{2}(4xh) = x^2$

    $$2h = x$$
    $$h = \frac{x}{2}.$$

    The ratio of the altitude to a side of the square is $h : x = 1 : 2$.

19. <u>Solution 1</u>

    Draw $FEG \,||\, AD$. Then $AFGD$ is a

    parallelogram, and since $\triangle BFE \equiv \triangle CGE$, its area
    is equal to that of trapezoid $ABCD$.

    The area of trapezoid $ABCD$ is $\dfrac{1}{2}(9 + 5)10 = 70$.

    Since $\triangle ADE$ and parallelogram $AFGD$ have the
    same base and the same height,

    the area of $\triangle ADE$ is $\dfrac{1}{2}AFGD = 35$.

    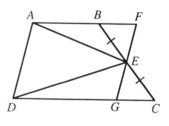

    <u>Solution 2</u>

    Draw $EH \,||\, DC$. Since $BE = EC$ and

    $AB \,||\, EH \,||\, DC$,

    $EH = \dfrac{1}{2}(AB + DC) = 7$.

    Therefore $\triangle ADE = \triangle AHE + \triangle HDE$

    $\qquad\qquad\quad = \dfrac{1}{2}\,EH$ (sum of altitudes)

    $\qquad\qquad\quad = \dfrac{1}{2}\,(7)(10)$

    $\qquad\qquad\quad = 35$.

    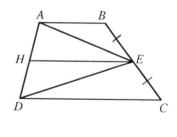

20. From the given ratios, the lengths of line segments
    can be marked as indicated.

    $\triangle GEF$

    $=$ square $ABCD - [\triangle ECF + \triangle GDF + \text{trapezoid } ABEG]$

    $= 144 - \left[\dfrac{1}{2}(8 \times 9) + \dfrac{1}{2}(4 \times 6) + \dfrac{1}{2}(3 + 6)\,12\right]$

    $= 42$.

    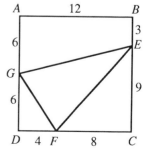

21. The shortest altitude is drawn to the longest side, and the longest altitude is drawn to the shortest side. Hence, if m is the longest altitude, using areas, we obtain

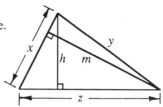

$$\frac{1}{2}mx = \frac{1}{2}hz$$
$$m = \frac{hz}{x}.$$

22. In a scalene triangle there are no equal sides and the sum of any two sides must exceed the third. If the perimeter is less than 13, the longest side must be less than 6 because the perimeter cannot be greater than 12. If the greatest side is 5, the other sides must have a sum of 6 or 7. The only possibilities are a triangle of sides 5, 4, 3, or one of sides 5, 4, 2. If the longest side is 4 the other sides must be 3 and 2. There are three such triangles.

23. $AB = EF = \frac{1}{3}(12) = 4$ and

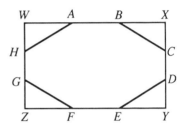

$CD = GH = \frac{1}{3}(9) = 3$.
$AH = BC = DE = FG$, and in $\triangle WHA$,
$WA = 4$, $WH = 3$, so $HA = 5$.
The perimeter is $2 \times 4 + 2 \times 3 + 4 \times 5 = 34$.

24. <u>Solution 1</u>
    There are two possible diagrams. The solution here is based on the diagram shown. It can easily be adapted for the second possibility. From the symmetry of the diagram let $EA = ED = x$. Then $EC = EB = 4 - x$.

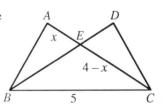

Since $AB = 3$, $AC = 4$, and $BC = 5$, $\angle A = 90°$.
    Therefore $3^2 + x^2 = (4 - x)^2$
$$x = \frac{7}{8}.$$
$$\triangle BEC = \triangle ABC - \triangle ABE$$
$$= \frac{1}{2}(3)(4) - \frac{1}{2}(3)\left(\frac{7}{8}\right)$$
$$= 6 - \frac{21}{16}$$
$$= 4\frac{11}{16}.$$

Solution 2

If *EF* is perpendicular to *BC*, then, by symmetry,
EB = *EC* and *F* is the midpoint of *BC*.
Δ *BEF* is similar to Δ*BCD* since all angles are
equal.

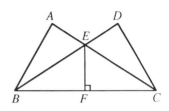

Hence $\dfrac{EF}{DC} = \dfrac{BF}{BD}$

$$\dfrac{EF}{3} = \dfrac{\frac{5}{2}}{4}$$

$$EF = \dfrac{15}{8}.$$

The area of Δ*EBC* is $\dfrac{1}{2}\left(\dfrac{15}{8}\right)(5)$

$$= 4\dfrac{11}{16}.$$

25. If *AB* = *x* and *BI* = *y*, then *xy* = 6 where *x*, *y*
are integers.
If *ID* = *a* and *DE* = *b*, then *ab* = 15 where *a*, *b*
are integers.
Then $(x, y) = (1, 6), (2, 3), (3, 2),$ or $(6, 1),$
and $(a, b) = (1, 15), (3, 5), (5, 3),$ or $(15, 1).$
Also, the area of *ACEG* is

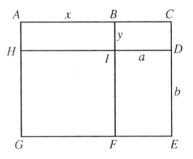

$$(x + a)(y + b) = xy + ab + xb + ya$$
$$= 21 + xb + ya.$$

To maximize the area, we wish to pick the values of *x*, *y*, *a*, *b*, which make *xb* + *ya*
as large as possible. We need not try all sixteen pairings because trying (1, 6) with the
four (*a*, *b*) pairs is equivalent to trying (6, 1) with them.

Hence consider (1, 6) with each of (1, 15), (3, 5), (5, 3), (15, 1), then (2, 3) with
these four.

The maximum occurs for $xb + ya = 6(15) + 1(1) = 91.$

The maximum area is 112.

Number Theory

Multiple Choice Questions

1. The number obtained when the digits are in descending order is 9431.
    The number obtained when the digits are in ascending order is 1349.
    The difference between the numbers is 8082.
    The answer is B.

2. The smallest such integer is 1023 and the largest is 9876.
    Their difference is $9876 - 1023 = 8853$.
    The answer is C.

3. When the odometer reads 2777 km, the car will have travelled $2777 - 2722 = 55$ km.
    The answer is B.

4. $3 \times 10^5 + 4 \times 10^3 + 7 \times 10^2 + 5 = 300\ 000 + 4000 + 700 + 5 = 304\ 705$.
    The answer is A.

5. By noting that $r - 9$ gives 8 we conclude that we must borrow 10 from q in order to subtract. The question can be successfully handled by following this line of reasoning.
    However, it is far easier to note that for the subtraction to be correct, then

    k 3 5 9
    $+ \underline{1\ 5\ 8\ 8}$
    6 p q r

    And now we quickly obtain $r = 7, q = 4, p = 9, k = 5$.
    The answer is B.

6. The original number tu (in appearance) has value $10t + u$.
    The new number has appearance $t1u$, and its value is $100t + 10 + u$.
    The answer is D.

7. In base 4, the significance of writing 1, 2, 3, 10, 11, 12, 13, 20, ... is that
    $$10 = 1 \times 4 + 0, \quad 11 = 1 \times 4 + 1, \quad 12 = 1 \times 4 + 2, \quad 20 = 2 \times 4 + 0, \text{ etc.}$$
    Hence, in base 4, the twentieth number is
    $$20 = 16 + 4 + 0$$
    $$= 1 \times 4^2 + 1 \times 4 + 0,$$
    and the number is written 110.
    The answer is E.

8. Let the 3-digit number be $M = 100a + 10b + c$ and let the number with the order of
    the digits reversed be $N = 100c + 10b + a$, with $M \geq N$.
    Then $x = M - N$
    $$= (100a + 10b + c) - (100c + 10b + a)$$
    $$= 99(a - c).$$
    Since x is non-negative, $a \geq c$.
    Hence $a - c = 0, 1, 2, 3, 4, 5, 6, 7,$ or 8.
    Therefore x can be any of the 9 multiples of 99 from 0 to 792 inclusive.
    The answer is B.

9. The square root of $8mn9$ is a two-digit number and it must end in 3 or 7 because no
    other digit when squared gives a number ending in 9.
    Also, since the square begins with 8, the two-digit number is at least 90 since
    $90^2 = 8100$ and $89^2 < 8000$.
    By trial, $93^2 = 8649$ and $97^2 > 9000$.
    Therefore, $m + n = 6 + 4 = 10$.
    The answer is D.

10. Since bcd is divisible by 5, $d = 5$.
    Since cde is divisible by 3, $c + d + e$ is also divisible by 3.
    The only possibilities for cde are 153, 351, 354, 453.
    But abc is divisible by 4.
    Therefore $c = 4$.
    Finally abc must be 124 or 214.
    Since 214 is not divisible by 4, $abcde$ is 12453.
    Hence $a = 1$.
    The answer is A.

11. Consider each of the 3-digit numbers:
    $BAD = 100B + 10A + D,$
    $DAM = 100D + 10A + M,$
    $MAD = 100M + 10A + D,$
    Their sum is $102D + 101M + 100B + 30A$
    To make the sum a maximum, we should set $D = M = 9, B = 8,$ and $A = 1$.
    Then the sum is 2657.
    The answer is D.

12. Solution 1

Between 100 and 199 there are 10 integers in which the sum of the digits is 10, namely 109, 118, 127, 136, 145, 154, 163, 172, 181, and 190.

Between 200 and 299 there are 9 integers in which the sum of the digits is 10, namely 208, 217, 226, 235, 244, 253, 262, 271, and 280.

Similarly, in the 300s, 400s,..., 900s there are 8, 7, ..., 2 such integers respectively.

The total number of integers between 100 and 1000 such that the sum of their digits is 10 is $10 + 9 + 8 + 7 + 6 + 5 + 4 + 3 + 2 = 54$.

Solution 2

When considering the sum of digits in numbers, one can frequently avoid lengthy searching by representing possible numbers by variables, one for each digit. Here, for example, consider the possible 3-digit numbers between 100 and 1000 as xyz, where $x \geq 1$, $y \geq 0$, $z \geq 0$, and $x + y + z = 10$.

Clearly x can be 1, 2, 3, ..., 9, and for each of these a simple equation in y and z results.

Thus if $x = 1$, $y + z = 9$ and there are 10 possible numbers, using (0,9), (1,8), ..., (9,0), to obtain 109, 118, ..., 190.

If $x = 2$, $y + z = 8$ and there are 9 possible numbers.

If $x = 3$, $y + z = 7$ and there are 8 possible numbers.

Continuing, if $x = 9$, $y + z = 1$ and there are 2 possible numbers.

Hence, the number of 3-digit numbers is $N = 10 + 9 + 8 + ... + 4 + 3 + 2$.

Sums such as this can be evaluated by simply adding, but if the string is lengthy this is time consuming. Note that the average of 10 and 2 is 6, for 9 and 3 is 6, and indeed for every pair working from the ends the average is 6. Thus the sum can be obtained from the product of the average of pairs (counting form the ends inwards) and the number of terms; in this case $\dfrac{10+2}{2} \times 9 = 54$.

(Try this method on $10 + 11 + 12 + ... + 98 + 99 + 100$.)

The answer is B.

Full Solution Questions

1. The largest possible number is 9754.
   The smallest possible number is 4579.
   The sum of these numbers is 14 333.

2. Since $8 \times Q$ ends in a zero and Q cannot be 0, Q is 5. Then $P8 \times 35 = 2730$ or $P8 = 2730 \div 35$.
   Hence, $P8$ is 78 and P is 7.
   Therefore P is 7 and Q is 5.

3. Solution 1
    One approach is to change the given numbers to base 10, find their sum, and change this back to base 8.

    Hence, $267_8 = 2 \times 8^2 + 6 \times 8 + 7$
    $$= 183 \text{ (base 10)}$$
    $$135_8 = 1 \times 8^2 + 3 \times 8 + 5$$
    $$= 93 \text{ (base 10)}$$
    $$183 + 93 = 276 = 4 \times 8^2 + 2 \times 8 + 4$$
    $$= 424_8.$$

    Solution 2
    Numbers can be added directly in base 8 by noting that $7 + 5 = 1 \times 8 + 4 = 14$ (base 8), and so on.

    Thus, 267_8
    $+$ 135_8
    $424_8.$

4. Solution 1
    Working in base 5, we have: 11000
    $$-3124$$
    $$2321.$$
    The difference to be paid is 2321 Martian dollars.

    Solution 2

    Changing from base 5 to base 10,
    $$11\,000_5 = 1 \times 5^4 + 1 \times 5^3 = 750_{10}$$
    $$3124_5 = 3 \times 5^3 + 1 \times 5^2 + 2 \times 5 + 4 = 414_{10}.$$
    $$750 - 414 = 336$$
    $$336_{10} = 2 \times 125 + 75 + 10 + 1$$
    $$= 2 \times 5^3 + 3 \times 5^2 + 2 \times 5 + 1$$
    $$= 2321_5.$$
    The difference is 2321 Martian dollars.

5. The next palindrome cannot occur until the initial 15 changes to 16, implying that the last two digits are 61.
    Thus the next palindrome is 16061, and the number of kilometres to be driven is 110.

6. <u>Solution 1</u>

Since the first digit is 5, the sum of the other two digits must be 7. The other pairs of possible digits are 7 and 0, 6 and 1, 5 and 2, 4 and 3. Since the order of each of these pairs can be reversed, there are 8 possible integers between 500 and 600 whose digits have a sum of 12.

<u>Solution 2</u>

List the possible integers, namely 507, 516, 525, 534, 543, 552, 561, and 570.

<u>Solution 3</u>

Consider the number as 5xy where x and y are the tens and units digits.

Then $5 + x + y = 12$

or $x + y = 7$.

Since x and y are digits, each must be chosen from 0, 1, 2, ..., 6, 7. Since $x + y$ is odd, then for each value of x there is exactly one value for y. There are eight possible values for x and hence there are eight possible three-digit numbers.

This solution allows one to determine the answer without determining the exact numbers, and is a much more attractive method for more difficult problems of this type.

7. Since bcd is divisible by 5, d must be 5 (0 is not allowed).

Now consider def, or 5ef. All multiples of 11 between 500 and 600 require either a digit greater than 6 or a zero, except for the one number, 561. Hence e is 6 and f is 1.

Next, since cde is divisible by 3, $c + d + e$ also is divisible by 3. We have $d = 5$ and $c = 6$ and 1 is already assigned, so c must be 4.

Lastly, since abc, or ab4, is divisible by 4 and only 2 and 3 are available for assignment, ab4 is either 234 or 324, and only the latter is divisible by 4.

Therefore, $a = 3, b = 2, c = 4, d = 5, e = 6, f = 1$.

8. For pages 1 to 9, a total of 9 digits was used.

For pages 10 to 99 a total of $2 \times 90 = 180$ digits was used.

There were $216 - 189 = 27$ digits remaining and these were sufficient to number 9 more pages with 3-digit numbers.

The number of pages in the book was $9 + 90 + 9 = 108$.

9. Let the number N expressed in base 9 be abc.
    Then $N = 9^2a + 9b + c = 81a + 9b + c$.
    N expressed in base 6 is cba, and each of a, b, c is 0, 1, 2, 3, 4, or 5.
    Now $N = 6^2c + 6b + a = 36c + 6b + a$.
    Hence $81a + 9b + c = 36c + 6b + a$
      or $80a + 3b - 35c = 0$.
    Since 5 divides $80a$ and $35c$, it must also divide $3b$.
    Therefore $b = 0$ or 5, and if $b = 0$, then $80a - 35c = 0$ or $16a - 7c = 0$, and there are
    no values of a and c which satisfy this equation for $a = 0$, 1, 2, 3, 4, or 5.
    Hence $b \neq 0$, and $b = 5$.
    The middle digit is 5.
    As an extension of this problem, it is a good exercise to determine the number N in its
    base 9, base 6, and original base 10 forms.

10. Solution 1
    Let N be an integer of n digits, ending with a 4.
    We write $N = 10p + 4$ where p has $n - 1$ digits.
    Then $M = 4 \cdot 10^{n-1} + p$
    Now $M = 4N$ or $4 \cdot 10^{n-1} + p = 40p + 16$
    $$4 \cdot 10^{n-1} - 16 = 39p.$$
    Since the right side is divisible by 39, the left side must be as well. Factor the left side
    to obtain $16(25 \cdot 10^{n-3} - 1)$, where $25 \cdot 10^{n-3} - 1$ must be divisible by 39, so $n \geq 3$.
    We examine this expression for values of n.

n	$25 \cdot 10^{n-3} - 1$	
3	24	not divisible by 39
4	249	not divisible by 39
5	2499	not divisible by 39
6	24999	39×641

    Since n is the smallest value such that $25 \cdot 10^{n-3} - 1$ is divisible by 39, we conclude
    that N has at least six digits.
    We challenge the reader to determine other possible values!

Solution 2 (This solution achieves an answer, but does not address the question of other values.)
Since N ends in 4 and $M = 4N$, M must end in 6.
Then N ends in 64 and M must end in 56.
Then N ends in 564 and M must end in 256.
Then N ends in 2564 and M must end in 0256.
Then N ends with 02564 and M must end with 10256.
Then N is 102564 and M is 410256.
N contains six digits.

11. If a is a digit in X and b is the corresponding digit in Y, then there are two cases:

   1. $a + b$, including any carry from the previous column, is equal to or less than 9. Then the sum $(a + b)$ contributes exactly this value to the total sum.

   2. $a + b$, together with any carry from the previous column is equal to or greater than 10. Then $a + b$ contributes $a + b - 10$ to the sum in this column, but contributes a carry of 1 in the next column, so the total contribution is $a + b - 9$. Hence the sum of the digits in $X + Y$ is the sum of the digits in X and the sum of the digits in Y minus nine times the number of carries.
      The sum of the digits is $53 + 47 - 45 = 55$.

12. Their ages must be two-digit numbers, for if either is one-digit the other must be three digits, and when 31 is added to the one-digit age the result is a two-digit number. Hence the adjusted sum would be five digits. Hence let Anne's age be x and Tom's age be y where x and y are two-digit numbers. Then $100x + y$ is a square and we write
   $100x + y = k^2, \; k > 0$.
   Similarly, considering their ages 31 years form now, they must be two-digit numbers, and we write
   $100(x + 31) + (y + 31) = m^2, \; m > 0$.
   Subtracting, $100(31) + 31 = m^2 - k^2$
   $\qquad$ or $101 \times 31 = (m - k)(m + k)$.
   Since 31 and 101 are primes and since $(m + k) > (m - k)$,
   $m + k = 101$
   $m - k = 31$.
   Solving, $k = 35$.
   Hence, $100x + y = 35^2 = 1225$.
   Therefore Anne is 12 years old and Tom is 25.

Similar Triangles

Multiple Choice Questions

1. Let AB and CD respresent the tree and the stake, respectively.

    Since $\triangle ABC \sim \triangle CDE$,

    $$\frac{AB}{CD} = \frac{BE}{DE}$$

    $$\frac{AB}{3} = \frac{63}{7}.$$

    Hence $AB = \dfrac{63(3)}{7} = 27$ feet.

    The answer is D.

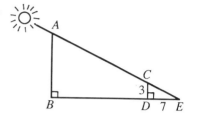

2. Since $\triangle APQ \sim \triangle ABD$,

    $$\frac{AP}{AB} = \frac{PQ}{BD}$$

    Therefore $\dfrac{x}{x + 10} = \dfrac{2}{8}$

    $$8x = 2x + 20$$

    $$x = \frac{10}{3}.$$

    The length of the ramp is $\dfrac{10}{3} + 10 = \dfrac{40}{3}$ feet.

    The answer is E.

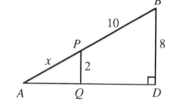

3. Since $AB = 4$ and $AC = 3$, $BC = 5$.

    Since Y is the midpoint of CB, $BY = \dfrac{5}{2}$.

    Since triangles XBY and CBA are similar,

    $$\frac{BA}{BY} = \frac{AC}{XY}$$

    $$\frac{4}{\frac{5}{2}} = \frac{3}{XY}.$$

    Hence, $XY = \left(\dfrac{5}{2}\right)\left(\dfrac{3}{4}\right) = \dfrac{15}{8}$.

    The answer is C.

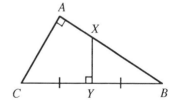

4. Draw PZ perpendicular to QR.

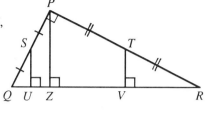

Since S is the midpoint of PQ and $SU \| PZ$,
$QU = UZ$ and $SU = \dfrac{1}{2}PZ$.

Similarly, $ZV = VR$ and $TV = \dfrac{1}{2}PZ$.

Therefore $\triangle SQU = \dfrac{1}{4}\triangle PQZ$ and
$\triangle TVR = \dfrac{1}{4}\triangle PZR$.

Hence $\triangle SQU + \triangle TVR = \dfrac{1}{4}\triangle PQR$.

Therefore $SUVTP = \dfrac{3}{4}\triangle PQR$.

The answer is E.

5. Since A, B, and C lie in a straight line,
slope AB = slope BC.

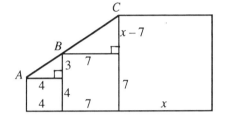

Therefore $\dfrac{3}{4} = \dfrac{x-7}{7}$

$4x - 28 = 21$

$4x = 49$

$x = \dfrac{49}{4}$.

The answer is B.

6. Since $PQ \| BC$, $\angle AQP = \angle ABC$ and
$\angle APQ = \angle ACB$.

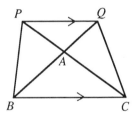

Therefore $\triangle ABC$ is similar to $\triangle AQB$.

Hence $\dfrac{PQ}{BC} = \dfrac{PA}{AC} = \dfrac{QA}{AB} = \dfrac{2}{3}$.

Since $\triangle PAB$ and $\triangle ABC$ have a common altitude
from B, $\triangle PAB = \dfrac{2}{3}\triangle PAB = 24$.

Similarly, $\triangle QAC = \dfrac{2}{3}\triangle ABC = 24$.

$\triangle PAQ = \dfrac{2}{3}\triangle PAB = 16$.

Thus the area of $PBCQ = 24 + 24 + 16 + 36 = 100$.

The answer is D.

7. Draw altitudes AX and AY.

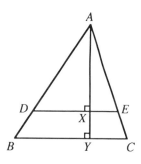

$$\frac{\triangle ADE}{\triangle ABC} = \frac{\frac{1}{2} DE \cdot AX}{\frac{1}{2} BC \cdot AY} = \frac{2}{3}.$$

Since $\triangle ADX \sim \triangle ABY$ and $\triangle ADE \sim \triangle ABC$,

$$\frac{AX}{AY} = \frac{AD}{AB} = \frac{DE}{BC}.$$

Therefore, $\dfrac{DE \cdot AX}{BC \cdot AY} = \dfrac{DE^2}{BC^2} = \dfrac{2}{3}$

$$DE^2 = \frac{2}{3}(144) = 96$$

$$DE = \sqrt{96} = 4\sqrt{3}.$$

The answer is B.

8. Solution 1

Let $AE = y$, $BE = x$, $DC = k$, and $AB = 1$.

Since $AB \parallel CD$, triangles AEB and ECD are similar.

Therefore $DE = kx$ and $CE = ky$.

Draw $AF, BG \perp DC$ and let $AF = h, DF = z,$

$GC = w.$

$$AD^2 - BC^2 = (h^2 + z^2) - (h^2 + w^2) = z^2 - w^2$$
$$= (z - w)(z + w) = (z - w)(k - 1).$$
$$DB^2 - AC^2 = [h^2 + (z + 1)^2] - [h^2 + (w + 1)^2]$$
$$= (z^2 - w^2) + 2(z - w)$$
$$= (z - w)(z + w + 2) = (z - w)(k + 1).$$

Therefore, $\dfrac{AD^2 - BC^2}{DB^2 - AC^2} = \dfrac{(z - w)(k - 1)}{(z - w)(k + 1)} = \dfrac{k - 1}{k + 1}.$

Solution 2

Let $AE = y$, $BE = x$,

and $\angle AED = \angle BEX = \theta$.

Since $AB \parallel CD$, then triangles AEB and ECD

are similar.

Therefore, $DE = kx$ and $CE = ky$.

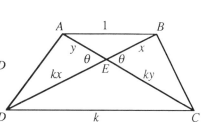

$$\frac{AD^2 - BC^2}{DB^2 - AC^2} = \frac{[(kx)^2 + y^2 - 2kxy \cos \theta] - [x^2 + (ky)^2 - 2kxy \cos \theta]}{(k+1)^2 x^2 - (k+1)^2 y^2}$$

$$= \frac{k^2x^2 + y^2 - x^2 - k^2y^2}{(k+1)^2 (x^2 - y^2)} = \frac{(k^2 - 1)(x^2 - y^2)}{(k+1)^2 (x^2 - y^2)}$$

$$= \frac{(k-1)(k+1)}{(k+1)^2} = \frac{k-1}{k+1}.$$

The answer is E.

9. Since *EG* joins the midpoints of *FC* and *BC*,
   EG is parallel to *BF*.
   Similarly, *HG* joins the midpoints of *BC* and *BF*,
   so *HG* is parallel to *FC*.
   Hence *FHGE* is a parallelogram.
   The answer is E.

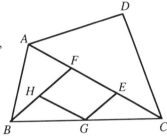

10. <u>Solution 1</u>
    Since triangles *ADF* and *ABC* are similar, their
    areas are proportional to the squares of the lengths
    of their corresponding sides.

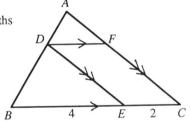

$$\frac{\triangle ADF}{\triangle ABC} = \left(\frac{DF}{BC}\right)^2 = \left(\frac{EC}{BC}\right)^2 = \left(\frac{2}{6}\right)^2 = \frac{1}{9}.$$

Hence $\triangle ADF = \frac{1}{9} \triangle ABC$.

Also, $\frac{\triangle BED}{\triangle ABC} = \left(\frac{BE}{BC}\right)^2 = \left(\frac{4}{6}\right)^2 = \frac{4}{9}$.

Hence $\triangle BED = \frac{4}{9} \triangle ABC$.

By subtraction, $DECF = \frac{4}{9} \triangle ABC$.

Thus $\frac{DECF}{\triangle ADF} = \frac{\frac{4}{9} \triangle ABC}{\frac{1}{9} \triangle ABC} = \frac{4}{1}.$

Solution 2

Since triangles ADF, BDE, and ABC are similar,

$$\frac{\Delta ADF}{DF^2} = \frac{\Delta BDE}{BE^2} = \frac{\Delta ABC}{BC^2} = k.$$

Then $\Delta ADF = 4k$, $\Delta BDE = 16k$, $\Delta ABC = 36k$.

By subtraction, $DECF = 36k - 16k - 4k = 16k$.

Hence $\dfrac{DECF}{\Delta ADF} = \dfrac{16k}{4k} = \dfrac{4}{1}$.

The answer is A.

11. If $AE = x$, then $ED = 2x$ and $BC = 3x$.
    The area of similar triangles are proportional to the
    squares of the lengths of their corresponding sides.

    Since $\Delta AEF \sim \Delta BFC$, then $\dfrac{\Delta AEF}{\Delta BFC} = \left(\dfrac{x}{3x}\right)^2 = \dfrac{1}{9}$.

    Also $\dfrac{AE}{BC} = \dfrac{EF}{FB} = \dfrac{1}{3}$.

    Since ΔAEF and ΔBFA have a common altitude

    from A, then $\dfrac{\Delta AEF}{\Delta ABF} = \dfrac{1}{3}$.

    Similarly, ΔABF and ΔBFC have a common

    altitude from B, so $\dfrac{\Delta ABF}{\Delta BFC} = \dfrac{1}{3}$.

    If $\Delta AEF = k$, then $\Delta ABF = 3k$ and
    $\Delta BFC = 9k$.
    Since $\Delta ABC = 12k$ and is half the parallelogram
    $ABCD$, then the area of $EFCD$ is $11k$.

    Thus, $\dfrac{\Delta ABF}{EFCD} = \dfrac{3k}{11k} = \dfrac{3}{11}$.
    The answer is D.

12. $\Delta CED = \dfrac{1}{2}\Delta CDB$

    $= \dfrac{1}{4}\Delta ABC$

    $= \dfrac{1}{8}\Delta AGB$

    $= \dfrac{1}{16}\Delta AGH$

    $= \dfrac{1}{32}\Delta GHK$

    $= \dfrac{1}{64}GHJK.$

    The answer is A.

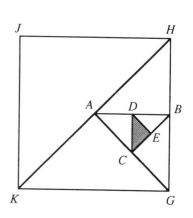

13. Since triangles AXZ and XYZ have a common altitude from Z and their bases AX and XY are in the ratio $1 : 2$, then

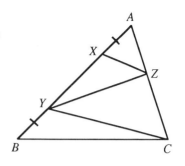

$$\frac{\Delta\ AXZ}{\Delta\ XYZ} = \frac{1}{2} = \frac{2k}{4k}.$$

Therefore, $\Delta AYZ = 6k$.

Similarly, $\dfrac{\Delta\ AYZ}{\Delta\ ZCY} = \dfrac{2}{3} = \dfrac{6k}{9k}.$

Hence $\Delta AYC = 15k$.

Also, $\dfrac{\Delta\ AYC}{\Delta\ BYC} = \dfrac{3}{1} = \dfrac{15k}{5k}.$

Finally, $\dfrac{\Delta\ BYC}{\Delta\ ZYC} = \dfrac{5k}{9k} = \dfrac{5}{9}.$

The answer is B.

14. Solution 1

Let coordinate axes lie along AB and AC.
Then the coordinates of B are $(12, 0)$.
Let the coordinates of C be $(0, 2b)$.
Since D and E are the midpoints of AC and BC, their coordinates are $(0, b)$ and $(6, b)$, respectively.

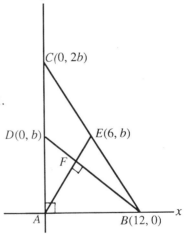

Since $AE \perp BD$, the product of their slopes is -1.

Hence, $\left(\dfrac{b}{6}\right)\left(\dfrac{-b}{12}\right) = -1$

$$b^2 = 72.$$

Therefore, $BC^2 = AC^2 + AB^2$

$$= 4b^2 + 144$$
$$= 4(72) + 144$$
$$= 432.$$

Hence, $BC = \sqrt{432}$

$$= 12\sqrt{3}.$$

Solution 2

Since AE and BD are medians, $AF = 2FE = 2x$
and $BF = 2FD = 2y$.

Since D and E are the midpoints of AC and BC
respectively, $DE = \frac{1}{2} AB = 6$.

In $\triangle DAB$, $9y^2 - DA^2 = 144$.

In $\triangle DAE$, $9x^2 - DA^2 = 36$.

Subtracting, $9(y^2 - x^2) = 108$

$$y^2 - x^2 = 12. \qquad (1)$$

In $\triangle DFE$, $\quad y^2 + x^2 = 36. \qquad (2)$

Therefore, $y^2 = 24$ and $x^2 = 12$.

Hence, $BC = 2BE$

$$= 2\sqrt{x^2 + 4y^2}$$
$$= 2\sqrt{12 + 96}$$
$$= 12\sqrt{3}.$$

The answer is E.

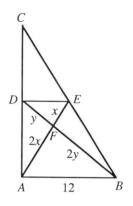

Full Solution Questions

1. Solution 1

The area of $\triangle ABC$ is $\frac{1}{2}(5)(10) = 25$.

The hypotenuse of $\triangle ABC$ is $\sqrt{100 + 25} = \sqrt{125}$.

Since the areas of similar triangles are proportional
to the squares of the lengths of their corresponding
sides,

$$\frac{\text{Area of } \triangle ABC}{\text{Area of } \triangle DEF} = \frac{15^2}{\sqrt{125}^2} = \frac{225}{125} = \frac{9}{5}.$$

Thus the area of $\triangle DEF$ is $\frac{9}{5}(25) = 45$.

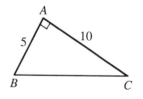

Solution 2

The sides of $\triangle ABC$ are 5, 10, and $5\sqrt{5}$.

Then $DE = 5\left(\frac{15}{5\sqrt{5}}\right) = 3\sqrt{5}$ and $DF = 10\left(\frac{15}{5\sqrt{5}}\right) = 6\sqrt{5}$.

The area of $\triangle DEF$ is $\frac{1}{2}(3\sqrt{5})(6\sqrt{5}) = 45$.

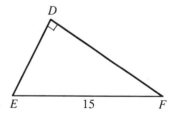

2. In the diagram, A is a right angle
    since $10^2 + 24^2 = 26^2$.

    Triangles BED and BAC are similar.

    Hence $\dfrac{BD}{BC} = \dfrac{DE}{24}$

    $\dfrac{5}{26} = \dfrac{DE}{24}$.

    Therefore $DE = \dfrac{5 \times 24}{26} = \dfrac{60}{13}$.

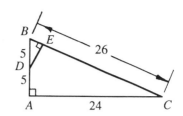

3. <u>Solution 1</u>

    Draw BF parallel to DE.
    Since $EC = 8$, then $AE = 4$ and $DE = \sqrt{25 - 16} = 3$.
    Since $DE \parallel BF$, $AE = EF = 4$ and $BF = 2DE = 6$.
    Therefore $BC = \sqrt{36 + 16} = \sqrt{52} = 2\sqrt{13}$.

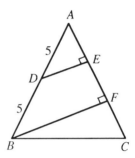

    <u>Solution 2</u>

    Draw $DG \parallel BC$.
    Then G is the midpoint of AC, $AG = 6$ and $EG = 2$.
    Since $AE = 4$, $DE = \sqrt{5^2 - 4^2} = 3$, and, in
    $\triangle DEG$, $DG = \sqrt{2^2 + 3^2} = \sqrt{13}$.
    Since $DG \parallel BC$ and D is the midpoint of AB,
    $BC = 2DG = 2\sqrt{13}$.

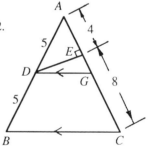

4. Let $BC = x$, $AB = 2x$, and $EF = y$.
    Then $CF = x - y$ and $AD = 2x - y$.
    Since $\triangle CEF$ is similar to $\triangle EAD$,

    $\dfrac{x - y}{y} = \dfrac{y}{2x - y}$

    $2x^2 - 3xy + y^2 = y^2$

    $2x^2 - 3xy = 0$.

    Since $x \neq 0$, $y = \dfrac{2x}{3}$.

    $\dfrac{\text{square } DEFB}{\triangle ABC} = \dfrac{y^2}{x^2} = \dfrac{\frac{4x^2}{9}}{x^2} = \dfrac{4}{9}$.

    The answer is E.

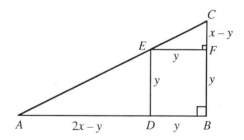

5. Extend *ED* and *AB* to meet at *K*.

    $AK = AB + DC = 8$.

    $KE = BC + DE = 5$.

    Since $\triangle ABN$ is similar to $\triangle AKE$,

    $$\frac{AB}{AK} = \frac{BN}{KE}$$

    $$\frac{4}{8} = \frac{BN}{5}$$

    $$BN = \frac{5}{2}.$$

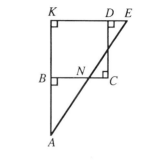

6. Let the medians meet at *O*.

    Then $OA = \frac{2}{3} AD$.

    Since $AX = \frac{3}{5} AD$, then $AX = \left(\frac{3}{5}\right)\left(\frac{3}{2}\right) OA = \frac{9}{10} OC$.

    Therefore $OX = \frac{1}{10} OA$.

    Similarly, $OY = \frac{1}{10} OB$ and $OZ = \frac{1}{10} OC$.

    Then $XY \parallel AB$, since *X* and *Y* divide
    OA and *OB* in the same ratio and it
    follows that $\triangle OXY$ is similar to $\triangle OAB$.

    Since the areas of similar triangles are proportional
    to the squares of the lengths of corresponding sides,

    $$\frac{\triangle OXY}{\triangle OAB} = \frac{XY^2}{AB^2} = \frac{1}{100}.$$

    Similarly, $\frac{\triangle OYZ}{\triangle OBC} = \frac{1}{100}$ and $\frac{\triangle OXZ}{\triangle OAC} = \frac{1}{100}$.

    Therefore $\frac{\triangle XYZ}{\triangle ABC} = \frac{1}{100}$.

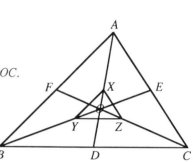

7. Since $\triangle EBC$ is isosceles, $BE = 8$ and $DE = 6$.

    Since $\triangle CED$ is similar to $\triangle BCE$,

    $$\frac{EC}{ED} = \frac{BC}{EC}$$

    $$EC^2 = (6)(8) = 48$$

    $$EC = 4\sqrt{3}.$$

    Since $\triangle CED$ is similar to $\triangle ABC$,

    $$\frac{EC}{DE} = \frac{AB}{BC}$$

    $$\frac{4\sqrt{3}}{6} = \frac{AB}{8}$$

    $$AB = \frac{8(4\sqrt{3})}{6} = \frac{16\sqrt{3}}{3}.$$

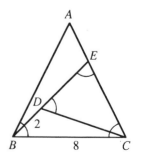

8. First we prove a useful geometry result, namely that the bisector of an angle of a triangle divides the opposite side in the same ratio as the sides about the angle, that is, $\dfrac{BD}{DC} = \dfrac{AB}{AC}$.

Draw $DE \perp AC$ and note that $DE = DB$ since D is on the bisector of $\angle BAC$.

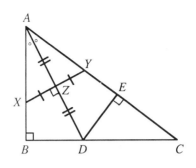

Then $\triangle DEC \sim \triangle ABC$ and thus $\dfrac{DE}{DC} = \dfrac{AB}{AC}$.

Since $DE = BD$, $\dfrac{BD}{DC} = \dfrac{AB}{AC} = \dfrac{3}{5}$.

Since $BC = 4$, $BD = \dfrac{3}{2}$, and $DC = \dfrac{5}{2}$.

In $\triangle ABD$, $AD = \sqrt{\dfrac{9}{4} + 9} = \dfrac{3\sqrt{5}}{2}$.

Since $\triangle AXZ \sim \triangle ADB$, $\dfrac{XZ}{BD} = \dfrac{AZ}{AB}$.

Therefore $XY = 2XZ = \dfrac{2BD \cdot AZ}{AB}$

$$= \dfrac{BD \cdot AD}{AB}$$

$$= \dfrac{\left(\frac{3}{2}\right)\left(\frac{3\sqrt{5}}{2}\right)}{3}$$

$$= \dfrac{3\sqrt{5}}{4}.$$

9. Let $BC = x$. Since triangles FAE and BCE are similar, $\dfrac{FA}{x} = \dfrac{FE}{EB} = \dfrac{18}{24}$.

Thus $FA = \dfrac{3x}{4}$ and $FD = \dfrac{1}{4}x$.

Since $\triangle FGD$ is similar to $\triangle BGC$,

$$\dfrac{FG}{BG} = \dfrac{FD}{BC}$$

$$\dfrac{FG}{FG + 42} = \dfrac{\frac{1}{4}x}{x} = \dfrac{1}{4}$$

$$4FG = FG + 42$$

$$FG = 14.$$

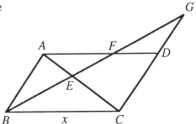

10. Join CD. Since $\triangle DBE$ and $\triangle DEC$ have a common altitude from D,

$$\frac{\triangle DBE}{\triangle DEC} = \frac{BE}{EC} = \frac{3}{4}.$$

Since $\triangle DBE = 6$, $\triangle DEC = 8$, and $\triangle DBC = 14$.

Similarly, $\dfrac{\triangle CAD}{\triangle CBD} = \dfrac{AD}{DB} = \dfrac{1}{2}.$

Since $\triangle DBC = 14$, then $\triangle CAD = 7$.

Therefore $\triangle ABC = \triangle DBC + \triangle CAD = 21$.

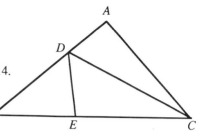

11. Solution 1

Join AD, cutting BE at G.

Since $\triangle ABG \sim \triangle ACD$,

$$\frac{BG}{13.2} = \frac{2.2}{8.8}, \text{ and so } BG = 3.3.$$

Since $\triangle AFD \sim \triangle GED$,

$$\frac{GE}{3.6} = \frac{GD}{AD} = \frac{BC}{AC} = \frac{6.6}{8.8}.$$

Thus $GE = 2.7$, and $BE = 3.3 + 2.7 = 6.0$.

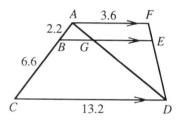

Solution 2.

Draw $AR \parallel FD$ to meet BE at S.

$SE = 3.6$ and $CR = 13.2 - 3.6 = 9.6$.

Since $\triangle ABS \sim \triangle ACR$,

$$\frac{BS}{CR} = \frac{AB}{AC}$$

$$\frac{BS}{9.6} = \frac{2.2}{8.8}.$$

Hence $BS = 2.4$ and $BE = 3.6 + 2.4 = 6.0$.

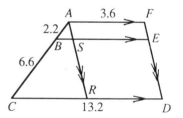

12. Triangles GDF, GEA, FBA, EDC, HBE, and HFC are all similar since they are equiangular. The areas of similar triangles are proportional to the squares of the lengths of their corresponding sides. If we let the areas of triangles GDF and HBE each be x, then the areas of triangles GEA and HFC are each $4x$, and the areas of triangles FBA and EDC are each $9x$.

Hence the area of parallelogram $EGFH$ is

$$9x - 4x - x = 4x.$$

The area of $ABCD$ is $2(\text{area of } \triangle EDC) = 18x$.

Therefore $\dfrac{\text{area } EGFH}{\text{area } ABCD} = \dfrac{4x}{18x} = \dfrac{2}{9}.$

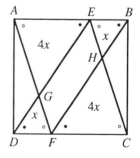

13. Solution 1

Impose a coordinate system on the diagram as shown. The required length, GF, is the y-coordinate of F.

The line through B and D has equation $y = \frac{30}{a}x$.

The line through A and E has equation

$y = -\frac{20}{a}x + 30$.

Point F is the intersection of these two lines.

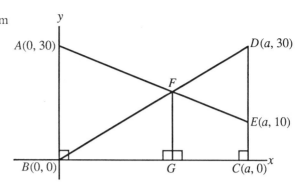

Since $x = \frac{ay}{30}$,

$y = \left(\frac{-20}{a}\right)\left(\frac{ay}{30}\right) + 30$

$\frac{5}{3}y = 30$

$y = 18$.

Solution 2

Since $DE : EC = 2 : 1$ and $DC = 30$, then $DE = 20$ and $EC = 10$.

Since $\triangle ABF$ is similar to $\triangle EDF$,

$\frac{BF}{FD} = \frac{AB}{DE} = \frac{30}{20} = \frac{3}{2}$.

Let $BF = 3m$, $FD = 2m$, and $BD = 5m$.

Since $\triangle BFG$ is similar to $\triangle BDC$,

$\frac{BF}{BD} = \frac{FG}{DC}$

$\frac{3m}{5m} = \frac{FG}{30}$.

Therefore $FG = \frac{3}{5}(30) = 18$.

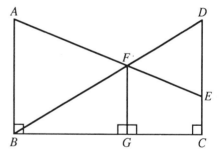

14. Draw DG parallel to BF.

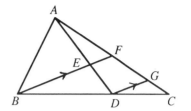

Since $\triangle AEF$ is similar to $\triangle ADG$,

$$\frac{AE}{ED} = \frac{AF}{FG} = \frac{5}{3}.$$

Since $\triangle CGD$ is similar to $\triangle CFB$,

$$\frac{BD}{DC} = \frac{FG}{GC} = \frac{5}{3}.$$

Therefore $\dfrac{AF}{FG} = \dfrac{25}{15}$, $\dfrac{FG}{GC} = \dfrac{15}{9}$.

Thus $AF : FG : GC = 25 : 15 : 9$.

Let $AF = 25k$, $FG = 15k$, $GC = 9k$.

Then $\dfrac{AF}{FC} = \dfrac{AF}{FG + GC} = \dfrac{25k}{15k + 9k} = \dfrac{25}{24}$.

Challenge Problems

Multiple Choice Questions

1. After the first exchange, there are 9 gallons of water and 36 gallons of wine in the cask. At this stage, the fraction of the mixture that is wine is $\frac{36}{45} = \frac{4}{5}$.
    When 9 gallons of the mixture are removed, the amount of wine removed is $\frac{4}{5} \times 9 = \frac{36}{5}$ gallons.
    The amounts of wine and water in the final mixture are $36 - \frac{36}{5} = \frac{144}{5}$ and $45 - \frac{144}{5} = \frac{81}{5}$ gallons, respectively.
    The ratio of water to wine is $\frac{81}{5} : \frac{144}{5}$, which is equivalent to 9 : 16.
    The answer is B.

2. Draw $PU \perp TS$.
    In right-angled triangle PUT,
    $$PT^2 = PU^2 + UT^2$$
    $$= 400 + 16$$
    $$= 416.$$
    In right-angled triangle PRT,
    $$PT^2 = PR^2 + RT^2$$
    $$= (8^2 + x^2) + [12^2 + (20 - x)^2]$$
    $$= 2x^2 - 40x + 608.$$
    Hence, $2x^2 - 40x + 608 = 416$
    $$x^2 - 20x + 96 = 0$$
    $$(x - 12)(x - 8) = 0.$$
    The possible values are $x = 12$ or $x = 8$.
    The answer is A.

    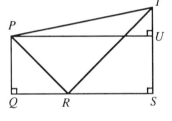

3. In the case where the centre of one circle lies outside the other circle, the circles would be tangent if $k = m + n$. To intersect in two distinct points points, $k < m + n$.

    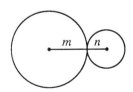

In the case where the centre of the smaller circle lies
inside the larger circle, the circles would be tangent
if $k = m - n$. To intersect in two distinct points,
$k > m - n$.

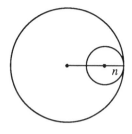

Hence, the circles intersect in two distinct points if
and only if k lies in the interval

$$m - n < k < m + n.$$

The answer is E.

4. Let the factors of $x^4 + rx^2 + s$ be $(x^2 + 4x^2 + 6)$ and $(x^2 + px + q)$.
    To find the value of r, s, p, and q, we multiply and compare coefficients.
    Thus, $x^4 + rx^2 + s = x^4 + (p + 4)x^3 + (q + 6 + 4p)x^2 + (4q + 6p)x + 6q$.
    The coefficients of x^3 and x are equal to 0.
    Hence, $p = -4$ and $q = 6$.
    Thus, $r = 6 + 6 - 16 = -4$, $s = 36$, and $r + s = 32$.
    The answer is B.

5. Using the second identity, $f(2137, 842)$ can be reduced as follows:
    $$\begin{aligned} f(2137,\ 842) &= f(2138,\ 841) \\ &= f(2139,\ 840) \\ &= f(2140,\ 839) \end{aligned}$$

    $$\vdots$$

    $$= f(2978,\ 1).$$
    Using the first identity we get $f(2978, 1) = 2978$.
    The answer is B.

6. The square of any real number is non-negative.
    Thus, $(a + b + c)^2 \geq 0$
    $$a^2 + b^2 + c^2 + 2(ab + bc + ca) \geq 0$$
    $$1 + 2(ab + bc + ca) \geq 0$$
    $$ab + bc + ca \geq -\frac{1}{2}.$$
    The minimum value of $ab + bc + ca$ is $-\frac{1}{2}$.
    The answer is E.

7. Since $a^x = c^q$, then $(a^x)^y = (c^q)^y$.
    Therefore, $a^{xy} = c^{qy}$
    $$= (c^y)^q$$
    $$= (a^z)^q$$
    $$= a^{zq}.$$
    Thus $xy = qz$.
    The answer is A.

8. Solution 1
    The factored form of $3x^2 + kxy - 2y^2 - 7x + 7y - 6$ is $(3x + Ay + B)(x + Cy + D)$.
    To find the values for A, B, C, D, we can expand and compare coefficients.
    Thus, $(B + 3D)x = -7x$ and $BD = -6$.
    Solving $B + 3D = -7$ and $BD = -6$ yields $B = 2$ and $D = -3$.
    Similarly, $(2C - 3A)y = 7y$ and $ACy^2 = -2y^2$.
    Solving $2C - 3A = 7$ and $AC = -2$ yields $A = -1$ and $C = 2$.
    Hence, $k = A + 3C = 5$.

    Solution 2
    The problem can be solved by considering the identity
    $$3x^2 + kxy - y^2 - 7x + 7y - 6 = (3x + Ay + B)(x + Cy + D).$$
    This identity will hold for all values of x and y.
    By choosing $y = 0$, the identity reduces to
    $$3x^2 - 7x - 6 = (3x + B)(x + D)$$
    $$(3x + 2)(x - 3) = (3x + B)(x + D).$$
    Thus, $B = 2$ and $D = -3$.
    Similarly, by choosing $x = 0$ in the original identity, we get
    $$-2y^2 + 7y - 6 = (Ay + 2)(Cy - 3)$$
    $$(-y + 2)(2y - 3) = (Ay + 2)(Cy - 3).$$
    Thus, $A = -1$ and $C = 2$.
    To obtain k, substitute $x = y = 1$ in the identity.
    $$3 + k - 2 - 7 + 7 - 6 = (3 - 1 + 2)(1 + 2 - 3)$$
    $$k = 5.$$
    The answer is D.

9. The diagram shows a top view of the cross-section
    taken 1" above the table top.
    The cross-section of the cylinder is a circle
    concentric with the circumcircle of the equilateral
    triangle formed by joining the centres of the ball
    bearings.

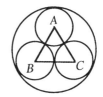

We now proceed to find the radius of the circumcircle of triangle ABC.

$AB = BC = CA = 2$

         (twice the radius of each ball bearing)

$BX = XC = 1$

$AX = \sqrt{4-1} = \sqrt{3}.$

Since $\triangle CXO \sim \triangle AXC$,

$\dfrac{OX}{1} = \dfrac{1}{\sqrt{3}}$ and $OX = \dfrac{1}{\sqrt{3}}.$

The radius of the circumcircle of triangle ABC is

$OA = OB = OC \quad = AX - OX$

$\qquad\qquad\qquad\qquad = \sqrt{3} - \dfrac{1}{\sqrt{3}}.$

Hence, the inner radius of the cylinder is

$\sqrt{3} - \dfrac{1}{\sqrt{3}} + 1 = \dfrac{2 + \sqrt{3}}{\sqrt{3}}$ inches.

The answer is E.

10. <u>Solution 1</u>

The graph of $y = \dfrac{3}{2-x}$ is the hyperbola shown.

The solution to the given inequality is the set of values of x for which the graph is on or below the line $y = 1$.

The line intersects the hyperbola at $(-1, 1)$.

The solution is $x \le -1$ or $x > 2$.

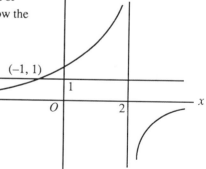

<u>Solution 2</u>

<u>Case 1</u>   For $2 - x > 0$, or $x < 2$,

$\qquad\qquad 3 \le 2 - x$

$\qquad\qquad x \le -1.$

The values of x that satisy these conditions are $x \le -1$.

<u>Case 2</u>   For $2 - x < 0$, or $x > 2$.

$\qquad\qquad 3 \ge 2 - x$

$\qquad\qquad x \ge -1$

The values of x that satisfy these conditions are $x > 2$.

Combining the two cases yields the solution $x \le -1$ or $x > 2$.

The answer is D.

11. Since $z^x = y^{2x} = (y^2)^x$,

    then $z = y^2$.   (1)

    Since $2^z = 2(4^x)$

    $= 2(2^{2x})$

    $= 2^{2x+1}$,

    then $z = 2x + 1$.   (2)

    Substituting (1) into (2) gives

    $$x = \frac{y^2 - 1}{2}.$$

    We now substitute for x and z in $x + y + z = 16$ to get

    $$\frac{y^2 - 1}{2} + y + y^2 = 16$$
    $$3y^2 + 2y - 33 = 0$$
    $$(3y + 11)(y - 3) = 0.$$

    The possible values for y are 3 and $-\frac{11}{3}$.

    The answer is E.

12. We are given that the fifteen lines divide the plane into 121 non-overlapping regions, some completely bounded and some not.

    The unbounded regions will be on the periphery and formed by 30 rays. This creates 30 unbounded regions.

    Hence, the number of bounded regions is $121 - 30 = 91$.

    The answer is E.

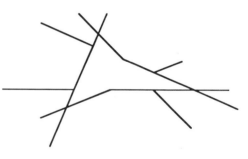

General Discussion

Consider the case of three existing lines satisfying the conditions of the problem. When a fourth line is added, it will have 3 intersection points with the existing lines, dividing it into 4 sections.

A new region is created for each section, in this case, 4 new regions.

In general when the nth line is added to the graph
created by $(n-1)$ lines, it will have $(n-1)$
intersection points, dividing it into n sections. This
creates n new regions.
If r_{n-1} represents the number of regions formed by
$(n-1)$ lines, then r_n, the number of regions
formed by n lines, is given by the recursion
formula

$$r_n = r_{n-1} + n$$

or $\quad r_n - r_{n-1} = n.$

Thus, $\qquad r_2 - r_1 = 2$

$$r_3 - r_2 = 3$$

$$\vdots$$

$$r_{15} - r_{14} = 15$$

_____

Add $\quad r_{15} - r_1 = 119.$

Since $r_1 = 2$, $r_{15} = 121.$
Also, n lines result in $2n$ unbounded regions, (see Solution 1).
The number of bounded regions is $121 - 30 = 91.$

13. We are given that $f(x-y) = f(x)\,f(y)$ for all x and y.
Choose $y = \frac{x}{2}$.

Thus, $\quad f\left(\frac{x}{2}\right) = f(x)\,f\left(\frac{x}{2}\right)$

$$f\left(\frac{x}{2}\right)[1 - f(x)] = 0.$$

Since $f\left(\frac{x}{2}\right) \neq 0$, then $1 - f(x) = 0$ which gives $f(x) = 1$, regardless of the value
for x.
Thus, $f(3) = 1.$
The answer is E.

Note:
One might use a special case of this solution by choosing x and y to have the values
3 and $\frac{3}{2}$, respectively. The solution follows the same as above, resulting in the
required value of $f(3)$.

Full Solution Questions

1. The prime factorization of 17 710 is $(2)(5)(7)(11)(23)$.
   Since the age of each person is at least twenty, then the factors $2, 5, 7, 11$ must be combined to form ages $2 \times 11 = 22$ and $5 \times 7 = 35$.
   The three ages are $22, 33$, and 35.

2. The place values in a number system with base 8 are $\ldots, 8^4, 8^3, 8^2, 8, 8^0 = 1$.
   Hence, $\quad 267 = \quad 2 \times 8^2 \qquad + 6 \times 8 \qquad + 7$
   $\qquad\qquad\quad 135 = \quad 1 \times 8^2 \qquad + 3 \times 8 \qquad + 5$
   Add $\qquad\qquad (3 \times 8^2) + (8 \times 8 + 1 \times 8) + (1 \times 8 + 4)$
   The sum is $4 \times 8^2 + 2 \times 8 + 4 = 424$.

3. $\qquad 7^y - 7^{y-2} = 336\sqrt{7}$
   $\qquad 7^{y-2}(7^2 - 1) = 336\sqrt{7}$
   $\qquad 7^{y-2}(48) = 336\sqrt{7}$
   $\qquad\quad 7^{y-2} = 7\sqrt{7} = 7^{\frac{3}{2}}$.
   Thus, $y - 2 = \dfrac{3}{2}$
   $\qquad\quad y = \dfrac{7}{2}$.

4. Let the speed of the train be d mph. This is equivalent to $\dfrac{5280d}{3600} = \dfrac{22d}{15}$ ft/s.
   Beginning with a click, numbered 0, we count subsequent clicks, $1, 2, 3, \ldots$, and must count d clicks, at which point the distance travelled will be $30d$ ft.
   The number of seconds required to travel $30d$ ft. at $\dfrac{22d}{15}$ ft/s is $\dfrac{30d}{\frac{22d}{15}} = \dfrac{225}{11}$.

5. Let the radius of the largest circle be R and the radius of the smaller circle which passes through point C be r.
   Thus $CD = 2R$, $CE = 2r$, and $ED = 2R - 2r$, and the radius of the third circle is $R - r$.
   Since $AB \perp CD$, $AE = EB = 5$.
   Since AB and CD are two intersecting chords of a circle,
   then $\quad 2r(2R - 2r) = (5)(5)$
   $\qquad\qquad Rr - r^2 = \dfrac{25}{4}$.

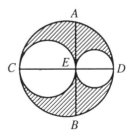

The area of the shaded region is

$$\pi R^2 - \pi r^2 - \pi(R-r)^2 = \pi[R^2 - r^2 - R^2 + 2Rr - r^2]$$
$$= \pi[2Rr - 2r^2]$$
$$= 2\pi\left(\frac{25}{4}\right)$$
$$= \frac{25\pi}{2} \text{ square units.}$$

6. $a^2 - 7a + b^2 - 7b + 2ab = 0$
    $$(a+b)^2 - 7(a+b) = 0$$
    $$(a+b)(a+b-7) = 0.$$
    Hence, $a + b = 0$ or $a + b - 7 = 0$.
    Since a and b are positive integers, $a + b \neq 0$.
    The solutions of $a + b = 7$ are

a	1	2	3	4	5	6
b	6	5	4	3	2	1

    There are six solutions.

7. Since $ABCDEFGH$ is a regular octagon, each of
    the diagonals AE, BF, CG, and DH is a diameter
    and each diameter subtends a right angle at P.
    Hence, $PA^2 + PE^2 = 4$
    $$PB^2 + PF^2 = 4$$
    $$PC^2 + PG^2 = 4$$
    $$PD^2 + PH^2 = 4.$$
    Adding $PA^2 + PB^2 + ... + PH^2 = 16$.

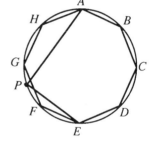

8. $x^2 + 3xy + y^2 = 60$
    $$(x-y)^2 + 5xy = 60$$
    $$5xy = 60 - (x-y)^2$$
    $$xy = 12 - \frac{1}{5}(x-y)^2.$$
    Since $(x-y)^2 \geq 0$, xy will be maximized when $\frac{1}{5}(x-y)^2 = 0$.
    The maximum value of xy is 12 and occurs when $x = y = \sqrt{12}$.

9. We want to determine the number of ordered triples (x, y, z) of integers satisfying
    $|x| \cdot |y| \cdot |z| = 12$.
    Consider the case where x, y, z are all positive.
    The integer solutions having a product of 12 are the 18 ordered triples listed.

x	12	1	1	6	6	2	2	1	1	4	4	3	3	1	1	3	2	2
y	1	12	1	2	1	6	1	6	2	3	1	4	1	4	3	2	3	2
z	1	1	12	1	2	1	6	2	6	1	3	1	4	3	4	2	3	3

For each of the absolute value signs, the number of solutions doubles since the positive integer can be replaced by its negative with no change in the product. Thus, the total number of integral solutions is $18 \times 2 \times 2 = 144$.

10. The densest packing of the quarters in the triangular frame would be one which has the quarters mutually tangent and placed in rows of 1, 2, 3, ..., k quarters.

    Since $1 + 2 + 3 + ... + 14 = 105$, there are 14 quarters in the base row.

    Let the radius of each quarter be r. The side AB of the triangular frame has length $2AD + 26r = 14$.
    Since ADE is a 30° – 60° – 90° triangle, $AD = \sqrt{3}r$.
    Thus, $2\sqrt{3}r + 26r = 14$.
    and $r = \dfrac{14}{26 + 2\sqrt{3}} = \dfrac{7}{13 + \sqrt{3}}$ inches.

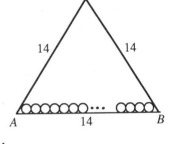

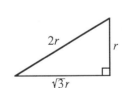

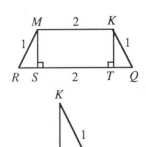

11. Solution 1

    Consider the isosceles trapezoid $MRQK$.
    Since $MK \parallel RQ$, $\angle MKQ = 120°$,
    then $\angle KQR = 60°$.
    Similarly, $\angle MRQ = 60°$.
    Draw MS and KT perpendicular to RQ.
    Let MK have length 2.
    Thus, $MR = KQ = 1$.
    Triangles MRS and KTQ can be combined to form an equilateral triangle having sides of length 1.
    Thus $RS + TQ = 1$, and $RQ = 3$.

The perimeter of $\triangle PQR$ is 9 and the perimeter of hexagon $DEFGKM$ is 12.
The ratio of these perimeters is 3 : 4.

<u>Solution 2</u>
Let the length of each side of the hexagon be 2.
Join M, K, Q, G to the centre of the circle that circumscribes the regular hexagon.
$\triangle OKG$ is equilateral with side of length 2.
Since Q is the midpoint of chord KG, $OQ \perp KG$ and $\angle KOQ = 30°$.
Hence, $OQ = \sqrt{3}$.
Draw $OV \perp RQ$.
Since $RQ \| MK$, OV bisects $\angle MOK = 60°$.
In triangle OVQ, $OQ = \sqrt{3}$.
Hence, $OV = \dfrac{\sqrt{3}}{2}$ and $VQ = \dfrac{3}{2}$.
Thus $RQ = 3$.
The perimeter of $\triangle PQR$ is 9 and the perimeter of hexagon $DEFGKM$ is 12.
The ratio of these perimeters is 3 : 4.

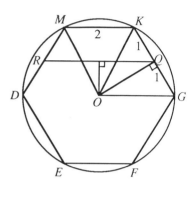

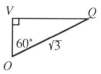

12. <u>Solution 1</u>
The crease formed is represented by FG.
Since A is the reflection of C in FG, FG is the right bisector of AC.
$AC^2 = 3^2 + 4^2 = 25$.
$AC = 5$.
$AE = EC = \dfrac{5}{2}$.
$\therefore \triangle GEC \sim \triangle ABC$, and so $\dfrac{EC}{BC} = \dfrac{GE}{AB}$

$$\dfrac{\frac{5}{2}}{4} = \dfrac{GE}{3}$$

$$GE = \dfrac{15}{8}.$$

Since $GE = EF$ ($\triangle AEF \equiv \triangle CEG$), the crease has length $\dfrac{15}{4}$.

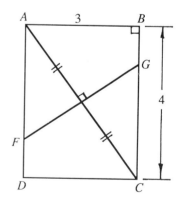

Solution 2

The rectangle is placed as shown with D at the origin, AD along the y-axis and DC along the x-axis. The midpoint of AC is E and it has coordinates $\left(\frac{3}{2}, 2\right)$.

The slope of AC is $-\frac{4}{3}$.

The equation of FG is
$$\frac{y-2}{x-\frac{3}{2}} = \frac{3}{4}$$

The coordinates of F and G are
$F\left(0, \frac{7}{8}\right)$, and $G\left(3, \frac{25}{8}\right)$.

The length of the crease FG is
$$\sqrt{9 + (\tfrac{18}{8})^2} = \sqrt{\frac{225}{16}}$$
$$= \frac{15}{4}.$$

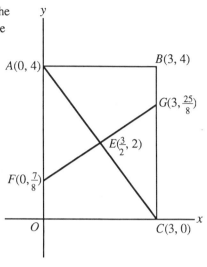

13. $(x + y + z)^3 = x^3 + y^3 + z^3 + 3x^2y + 3x^2z + 3y^2x + 3y^2z + 3z^2x + 3z^2y + 6xyz$

$= x^3 + y^3 + z^3 + (3x^2y + 3xy^2 + 3xyz) + (3x^2z + 3xz^2 + 3xyz)$

$\qquad\qquad\qquad\qquad\qquad\qquad\qquad + (3y^2z + 3yz^2 + 3xyz) - 3xyz$

$= x^3 + y^3 + z^3 + 3xy(x + y + z) + 3xz(x + y + z) + 3yz(x + y + z)$

$\qquad\qquad\qquad\qquad\qquad\qquad\qquad\qquad\qquad - 3xyz$

$= x^3 + y^3 + z^3 + (x + y + z)(3xy + 3xz + 3yz) - 3xyz.$

Since $x + y + z = 0$ and $xyz = 2$, upon substitution we get

$0 = x^3 + y^3 + z^3 + 0 - 6.$

Hence, $x^3 + y^3 + z^3 = 6$.

14. Solution 1

Let the missing digits be x and y.

The cost of the 72 turkeys was $(10000x + 6000 + 700 + 90 + y)$ cents.

Since no mention of weight is made, we must assume that the sale price was on a per turkey basis.

Thus, $10000x + 6790 + y$ is divisible by 72.

$10000x + 6790 + y = 72(138x + 94) + 64x + 22 + y$, and 72 must divide $64x + 22 + y$ as well.

Since $64x = 72x - 8x$, $-8x + 22 + y$ is divisible by 72.

x and y must be digits between 1 and 9 inclusive.

Hence, $-8x + 22 + y$ must be a value between $-8(9) + 22 + 1$ and $-8(1) + 22 + 9$, that is, between -49 and 23.

The only number in this interval divisible by 72 is 0.

Thus $\quad -8x + 22 + y = 0$

$$22 + y = 8x$$

The only feasible value of y that makes $22 + y$ divisible by 8 is 2.

The missing digits are $y = 2$ and $x = 3$, and the total cost of the turkey was \$367.92.

Solution2

Let the missing digits be x and y.

Since $72 = 8 \times 9$, then \$$x67.9y$ must be divisible by 8 and by 9.

A number is divisible by 8 if the number formed by the last 3 digits is divisible by 8.

In order for $79y$ to be divisible by 8, y must be 2. A number is divisible by 9 if the sum of its digits is divisible by 9.

In order for $x6792$ to be divisible by 9, $x + 6 + 7 + 9 + 2$ must be divisible by 9, and so x must be 3.

Therefore, the cost of the turkeys was \$367.92.

15. Since f is a real-valued function and $f(m + n) = f(m)f(n)$ for all m, n, we choose convenient values for m and n in order to discover the required relationship.

For $m = 4$ and $n = 0$ we have $f(4 + 0) = f(4) = f(4)f(0)$.

Hence $f(4)(f(0) - 1) = 0$.

Since $f(4) \neq 0$, $f(0) = 1$.

Also, $\quad f(4) = f(2 + 2) = f(2)f(2)$

$$= [f(2)]^2$$

$$= 256.$$

Thus, $f(2) = 16$ or -16.

But, $\quad f(2) = f(1 + 1) = f(1)f(1)$

$$= [f(1)]^2.$$

Hence, $f(2) \geq 0$, so $f(2) = 16$.

Since $0.0625 = \dfrac{1}{16}$, this suggests that $f(2)$ might be useful in obtaining the solution.

Using this insight along with $f(0) = 1$, we get

$$f(0) = f(2 + (-2))$$

$$= f(2)f(-2)$$

$$= 16f(-2)$$

$$= 1$$

This gives $f(-2) = \dfrac{1}{16} = 0.0625$ and $k = -2$.

Note: With further analysis one might deduce the given function to be $f(x) = 4^x$.